Prof. Sandy Primrose is a biologist wi
started his professional career as an
Edinburgh and Warwick and then mov
management positions in the pharmaceutical, life science, food and environmental sectors. This diverse background has given him a unique insight into plants and their uses. Sandy now has a mixed portfolio of interests that includes technology assessment, scientific writing, lecturing on science for the lay person and gardening.

Plants, Poisons And Personalities

by

Sandy Primrose

Librario

Published by

Librario Publishing Ltd.

ISBN: 978-1-906775-19-3

Copies can be ordered via the Internet
www.librario.com

or from:

Brough House, Milton Brodie, Kinloss
Moray IV36 2UA
Tel No 00 44 (0)1343 850 617

Printed and bound in the UK

Typeset by 3btype.com

Contents

Favourite Fruit And Vegetables

Noteworthy Trees

Roses And Orchids

Fascinating Flowers

The Close Of The Year

Foreword

This book was born out of frustration. As a keen gardener and a compulsive buyer of books I constantly examine the shelves of my local bookstore for the latest horticultural publications. Although there are plenty of new offerings, most of them are a disappointment to me because, reference books apart, I am looking for something that is educational and/or tells a story. Very few new plant books satisfy these criteria and this was the impetus for me to write this book. The original intention was to focus on the science behind plant breeding and cultivation. However, I open my garden for charity and often I have visiting groups that expect a guided tour. I try to make these visits both entertaining and educational by telling them the stories behind the plants that I grow. These stories always are well received and so I have chosen to make them the subject of this book. Furthermore, they have been written in the format of short essays to make them easy to read, particularly at bedtime.

Writing this book was a labour of love. Nevertheless I would like to dedicate it to the women in my life: Jill, Shonagh, Amy... and Beth!

Introduction

Linnaeus, Latin And Lust

Ask a botanist or a plantsperson the name of a plant and they will tell you its scientific (Latin) name. Non-gardeners find this infuriating for scientific names mean nothing to them. They want to know the common names of plants. So, why do we insist in using Latinized names? There are a number of reasons. First, common names can be very misleading, e.g. African marigolds do not come from Africa but from Mexico. Second, a particular plant can have different vernacular names in different places. *Aquilegia* is known as columbine and granny's bonnet and *Arum maculatum* is known as cuckoo pint, lords and ladies and countless other ruder names. Finally, a particular common name may refer to different plants in different countries. In England, the bluebell that carpets woods in Spring is *Hyacinthoides non-scripta* but this rapidly is being displaced by the larger and more vigorous Spanish bluebell, *Hyacinthoides hispanica*. The bluebells of Scotland, as popularized in the well-known song, are a totally different flower known to botanists as *Campanula rotundifolia* and in the United States bluebells are species of *Mertensia*. Only by using scientific names can we be sure that botanists in Acapulco, Adelaide, Amsterdam and Athens are talking about the same plant.

The science of classification is known as taxonomy and the Greek Theophrastus (370–285 BCE) is considered to be the father of taxonomy.

Theophrastus was a great scientific writer and amongst his publications were two large treatises on plants. In one of them, *Historia Plantarum*, he sketched out a plant taxonomy that was used up until the 18th century. The Romans, especially Pliny the Elder (23–79 CE) developed a significant interest in plants but when they referred to particular plants they used long, descriptive Latin sentences. Eventually the Roman system of nomenclature became too cumbersome and in the late 16th century Casper Bauhin developed a system using just two names. However, it was the efforts of Carl Linnaeus (1707–1778) that led to the widespread adoption of the binomial system for naming plants and all other living things.

The success of Linnaeus is somewhat surprising. A Swedish pastor and naturalist, he was considered by his peers as an ill-educated, provincial boor. At a time when religion was a key influencer of social behaviour, many of his rivals were trying to work out God's original blueprint for the universe. Despite being a pastor, Linnaeus devised a classification system that was not divinely ordained. This led one of his critics to comment that 'God created and Linnaeus classified'. Miaow! In 1753, Linnaeus published his 'Species Plantarum' which contained a straightforward system for correctly identifying plants. It was so simple that even women could understand it (his words, not mine!). Today, the names of nearly all plants date from this work or obey the conventions laid down in it.

In the Linnaean system, all living things have a name that consists of two parts: the genus or generic name and the species or specific epithet. Linnaeus used Latin to name organisms and this tradition has been retained for a number of reasons. First, Latin is a dead language and so the meanings of words do not change with time. Second, botanical Latin is very descriptive and has many terms for shape, texture and colour. Finally, the use of a dead language eliminates the parochial influence of the protagonists of the major European languages. A feature of the Linnaean system is that organisms are classified according to their assumed relatedness with the hierarchy being species, genus, family, order, class and division. Plants in the same genus are very closely related, e.g. *Geranium nodosum* and *G. wallichianum* and have similarities to other members of the same family, e.g. *Pelargonium* and *Erodium*.

The novel feature of the classification system introduced by Linnaeus was the ordering of plants numerically according to their reproductive organs, i.e. their flower structure. Plants with a similar flower structure are closely related. A good example is the family Papillionaceae where all the members, e.g. peas, beans, clovers, broom, laburnum, have flowers with the same characteristic shape. Given that Linnaeus lived in the highly chauvinistic society of the 18th century, his first level of plant ordering was based on the number of (male) stamens. Only sub-groups were determined by the number of (female) pistils. However, in describing his classification system, Linnaeus was unable to dissociate himself completely from his ecumenical training. Consider the following excerpt from his writings:

> The flowers leaves serve as bridal beds which the Creator has so gloriously arranged, adorned with such noble bed curtains, and perfumed with so many soft scents that the bridegroom with his bride might there celebrate their nuptials with so much the greater solemnity. When now the bed is so prepared, it is time for the bridegroom to embrace his beloved bride and offer her his gifts.

If Linnaeus was alive today he would be writing bodice rippers for Mills and Boon. So too would Erasmus Darwin (1731–1802), the grandfather of Charles Darwin. In his poem *The Temple of Nature* he wrote:

> The wakeful anther in his silken bed
> O'er the pleased stigma bows his waxen head;
> With the meeting lips and mingling smiles they sup
> Ambrosial dewdrops from the nectar'd cup;
> Or buoy'd in air the plumy lover springs'
> And seeks his panting-bride on hymen-wings.

The stamen males, with appetencies just,
Produce a formative prolific dust;
With apt propensities, the styles recluse
Secrete a formative prolific juice;
These in the pericarp erewhile arrive,
Rush to each other, and embrace alive.
Form'd by new powers progressive parts succeed
Join in one whole, and swell into a seed.

Originally, Linnaeus's writings were not well received. An 18th century edition of the *Encyclopaedia Britannica* commented that 'A man would not naturally expect to meet with disgusting strokes of obscenity in a system of botany, but … obscenity is the very basis of the Linnaean system'. This immediately conjures up images of young ladies swooning. As far as botanist Johann Siegesbeck was concerned, Linnaeus's ideas were 'loathsome harlotry'. How did Linnaeus respond to this slight? He ensured that the name Siegesbeck would forever be associated with an innocuous little weed that he called *Siegesbeckia.* Linnaeus instituted the practice whereby famous people, and not just botanists, are commemorated by having plants named after them. Occasionally the names selected were particularly appropriate. For example, he gave the name *Tillandsia* to the plants more commonly called 'air plants'. These plants do not require watering and the Latin name honours Pierre Tilland who had a pathological aversion to water! Given that Linnaeus was an extrovert and lover of flamboyant dressing was there a conscious decision by his fellow botanists to give his name to two relatively insignificant plants: *Linnaea borealis* and *Lobelia linnaeoides*?

A Presidential Plantsman

Thomas Jefferson (1743–1826) is best known as the third President of the United States of America (1801–1809) and the principal author of the Declaration of Independence. However, he also was a noted gardener and in 1811 wrote 'No occupation is so delightful to me as the culture of the earth, no culture comparable to that of the garden'. From 1769 his home was a property near Charlottesville, Virginia called Monticello and an image can be seen on US five cent coins (except those minted between 2003 and 2006). In a manuscript now known as the *Garden Book*, Jefferson kept records of the varieties of vegetables, fruits, flowers and trees that had been planted along with harvesting dates and notes about the weather.

The range of plants recorded by Jefferson reflects his broad interests and his curiosity. They include hot chilli peppers from an army captain in Texas, rare nectarines from Italy, and sweetcorn and bean varieties collected from native Indians during the Lewis and Clark expedition. Following his European travels, Jefferson introduced rhubarb, kale and a number of other vegetables to North America. His garden contained over 300 varieties of flowers, fruit and vegetables, many that he considered superior to the more-commonly grown varieties. Identifying many of these plants has proved difficult for many flowers and most vegetables are annuals and are easily lost if seed collection is neglected. Jefferson often listed plant varieties according to the person from whom he received it ('Leitch's pea'), its place of origin ('Tuscan bean') or a physical characteristic ('yellow carrot'). The present day curators of Monticello have tried to track down many of the plants described by Jefferson but the Taliaferro apple, the Hudson strawberry, the Monticello aspen and others remain unidentified or missing.

In 1803, Jefferson delivered a message to Congress outlining a plan for an exploration to the 'Western Ocean' (the Pacific) and requesting an appropriation of $2,500 for what would become the Lewis and Clark expedition. When the expeditionary group set out in May of that year one of their key goals was botanical discovery. This is not surprising given that Jefferson considered 'the greatest service that can be rendered any country is to add a useful plant to its culture'.

Among the many plants brought back for cultivation were the yellow Arika bean, named after the Arika Indians of Dakota, the Mad Dog Plant (*Echinacea angustifolia*) that was highly prized by native Americans for curing the bite of rattlesnakes and mad dogs, and the Osage orange (*Maclura pomifera*). The Osage orange (also known as 'bodark') was valued highly by the Osage Indians because its strength and elasticity made it ideal for tomahawks and bows. To the new inhabitants of North America, the chief virtue of the Osage orange was its ability to be grown as an impenetrable hedge with formidable thorns. By 1870 there were 60,000 miles of bodark hedging but its use declined following the invention of barbed wire for the latter did not need regular pruning. Ultimately Lewis and Clark were honoured botanically when the genera *Lewisia* and *Clarkia* were named after them.

Shortly after his request to Congress for funding for the Lewis and Clark expedition, Jefferson wrote to a friend 'When I return to Monticello I believe I shall become a florist'. In 18th century English a florist was a serious gardener who devoted his attention to carefully cultivating, observing, selecting and even systematically improving flowers for their beauty, fragrance, colour and grace. Jefferson also had a strong interest in economic botany and classified plants into four categories: medicinal, esculent (edible), ornamental and useful for fabrication. He also looked to plants for descriptive inspiration. In one letter to his granddaughter he used bulbs to illustrate the ephemeral nature of beauty and the normal transitions in life when he wrote:

> ...and the flowers come forth like the belles of the day, have their short reign of beauty and splendour, and retire, like them, to the more interesting office of reproducing their like. The Hyacinths and Tulips are off the stage, the Irises are giving place to the Belladonnas, as these will to the Tuberoses, etc...

As early as 1792, Jefferson had a reputation as a natural historian. Benjamin Smith Barton, the professor of botany at the University of Pennsylvania wrote 'In the various departments of this science, but especially in botany and zoology, the information of this gentleman is equaled by that of few persons in the United States'. If only we could say that about modern-day politicians! Barton's description of Jefferson was in support of a proposal to name a spring-blooming perennial of the woodlands of the eastern US as *Jeffersonia.* Soon *Jeffersonia* became a feature of the gardens of Philadelphians, but perhaps only of those with Republican leanings. By the time that Jefferson had retired from the presidency *Jeffersonia* had been introduced into British gardens by the Scottish plant collector John Lyons.

Jefferson had a mentor for his gardening efforts: Philadelphia nurseryman Bernard McMahon. As well as publishing the first seed catalogue in the United States, McMahon served as curator for the plants collected on the Lewis and Clark expedition. He successfully grew plants from seeds collected by Lewis and Clark from the woody shrub known as the Oregon Grape Holly and in 1818 botanist Thomas Nuttall called it *Mahonia aquifolium.* How fitting it is that both *Mahonia* and *Jeffersonia* should belong to the same plant family, the Berberidaceae.

The Planthunters Who Transformed Our Gardens

Most of the plants that we grow in our gardens are not native to our country or even our continent and yet all we have to do is go to a garden centre or specialist plant nursery and buy what we like. Seldom do we give much thought to how these plants reached our shores or to the intrepid explorers who literally risked life and limb to bring back exotic plants from far-off places. Without these planthunters our gardens would be much duller places. So, who were these men who sought out new plants for our delectation and to whom we owe so much?

Not all the exotic plants that we grow came through the efforts of planthunters. The first wave of plant introductions arrived in Britain with the Romans who brought with them important medicinal herbs and a second wave came following the Norman Conquest. Thereafter, new plants arrived in dribs and drabs from continental Europe as botanists and horticulturalists moved between countries. Some of these plants were not even native to Europe having arrived from Asia Minor or even the Orient via the overland caravan routes. The 15th century saw the start of the great sea explorations and botanists were key members of a ship's company. However, their task was to identify new crops with commercial value rather than plants of ornamental value.

The hunting of new plants for decorative purposes can be traced to the early 17th century and the four 'Johns': John Parkinson, John Tradescant the Elder, John Tradescant the Younger and John Evelyn. All four were friends and exchanged plants and correspondence. Parkinson grew many unusual plants in his garden but his main claim to fame is that he published in 1629 the first British gardening book. This contained a description of over 1,000 plants and extolled the virtues of cultivating plants for their beauty and pleasure. Evelyn also wrote textbooks on gardening but his main passion was trees. The writing of his most famous work, *Sylva: A Discourse of Forest Trees*, came about because of the acute shortage of trees for ship-building. The real planthunters were the two Tradescants, father and son.

Tradescant the Elder started his travelling by going to mainland Europe to buy fruit trees and tulip bulbs for his employer, Robert Cecil, the Earl of Salisbury who owned Hatfield House. After leaving Cecil he travelled to Russia and to Algiers and the North African coast. The latter trip was organized by the Royal Navy as part of a campaign to eliminate Barbary pirates but Tradescant managed to collect a number of interesting plants whenever there was a landfall. These included the Turpentine Tree (*Pistacia terebinthus*), Green Briar (*Smilax aspera*) and a number of rock roses (*Cistus* sp.). Tradescant the Younger had the same penchant for plant collecting that his father had but his travels took him west to the Caribbean and the Eastern seaboard of North America. Some of his finds include the Virginia Creeper (*Parthenocissus quinquefolia*), the Stag's Horn Sumach (*Rhus typhosa*), an insectivorous plant (*Sarracenia purpurea*) and the touch-sensitive mimosa (*Mimosa pudica*). Another plant that he collected is the spiderwort that now bears his name (*Tradescantia virginiana*, now *T x andersoniana*). The plant was supposed to be the antidote to the supposedly poisonous bite of the *Phalangium* spider hence the common name spiderwort.

David Douglas (1798–1834) was a gardener who started his career at the Glasgow Botanical Gardens. The Royal Horticultural Society recruited him as a plant collector and in 1824 he set off on an expedition to the Pacific Northwest via Cape Horn and the Galapagos. Over the next 10 years he brought many plants back to Britain including penstemons, camassias, lupins, the only North American peony, the flowering currant (*Ribes munroi*) and the Californian poppy (*Eschscholzia californica*). Douglas is best known for the large range of conifers that he brought back as seeds. These include the Douglas fir, named after him, as well as the Sitka spruce, sugar pine, western white pine, ponderosa pine, lodgepole pine, Monterey pine, grand fir, noble fir and others that have transformed the British landscape and timber industry. So successful was he at collecting pines that in one of his letters to his sponsor, Sir William Hooker, he wrote 'you will begin to think that I manufacture pines at my pleasure'. Unfortunately, his planthunting came to a premature end at the age of 35 when he died in mysterious circumstances in a bull pit in Hawaii.

The Industrial Revolution that swept through 19th century Britain provided a major impetus for plant collecting. Whilst creating ugly urban sprawl and the destruction of much of the countryside it fuelled the emergence of a class of nouveau riches who built large houses set in even larger grounds. Being the Victorian era, these wealthy individuals wanted formal or semi-formal gardens filled with attractive and novel plants, preferably ones that their neighbours did not have. A number of nursery firms were established to exploit this need and some of them even sponsored expeditions. This was the golden age of planthunting and the names of many of the individuals involved live on in the names of the plants that were collected by them and their peers. Only four of them will be detailed here: Reginald Farrer, George Forrest, Robert Fortune and Ernest Henry Wilson.

Reginald Farrer (1880–1920) was an unlikely candidate for a planthunter as he had suffered poor health since childhood. After studying at Oxford University he started exploring the plant life of the Alps but went on to visit Japan and China. Between 1914 and 1916 he collected plants in north-west China in a region close to the Mongolian and Tibetan borders. He sent back many plants and seeds of interest but most of these were lost as the majority of workers in botanical institutions had joined the army to fight in the First World War. One plant that did survive is the ever popular *Buddleja alternifolia*. After the war he made a trip to upper Burma, close to the border with China where he discovered the Chinese Coffin Tree (*Juniperus coxii*). Farrer never enjoyed good health and he died in Burma, the heat and stress of the expedition proving too much for him.

George Forrest (1873–1932) was employed by the Royal Botanic Gardens in Edinburgh and his planthunting efforts have resulted in the Gardens having the largest collection of wild-origin Chinese plants outside China. His first trip took place between 1904 and 1907 and was followed by six further expeditions, mainly to north-west Yunnan. Some of his adventures would do credit to Indiana Jones, especially on one trip when he was hunted for weeks by murderous Lamas and came close to death on a number of occasions. Eventually he escaped by crossing the Himalayas at 19,000 feet. Forrest was a prodigious collector and brought back over 300 new rhododendrons as well as camellias, magnolias, lilies, primulas, gentians and Himalayan poppies.

Robert Fortune (1812–1880) was another Scot who explored China. His sponsor, the Royal Horticultural Society, was reluctant to provide him with firearms but it was just as well that they did. Travelling by small boat along the Chinese coast his party was attacked by pirates. Fortune single-handedly drove them off. If that were not enough, he also managed to survive attacks by xenophobic mobs and horrendous storms in the South China Sea. Like George Forrest, Fortune's many adventures also would be a credit to Indiana Jones. Although he introduced many species that now are garden plants he is best known for establishing the tea plantations of India and Ceylon (Sri Lanka) thereby breaking the monopoly of China.

Nobody can better illustrate the trials and tribulations of being a plant hunter than Ernest Henry Wilson (1876–1930). In 1899 he was sent to China specifically to bring home seeds of *Davidia involucrata*, the pocket handkerchief tree. After landing in Hong Kong he travelled to central China to find the single specimen first discovered by Pere Amand David. Along the way he was imprisoned as a spy, nearly drowned on the Red River because his boatman was high on opium and then got caught up in the Boxer Rebellion. When he finally got to his destination he found that the tree had been chopped down to build a house. Fortunately, for his sanity, he found a whole grove of them and only later discovered that the race to collect the seeds had been won by a French nursery. Wilson probably was the greatest plant collector of all times and over 1,000 of his finds have been introduced into cultivation. The best known are the Kiwi fruit (*Actinidia deliciosa*) and the Regal Lily (*Lilium regale*). Whilst collecting the latter he was caught in a landslip that nearly cost him his leg. Before he could be rescued he had to lie on the ground and let a mule train pass over him. By contrast with his life, his death was quite mundane: he died in a car accident.

The golden age of plant hunting ended in the fifties with the death of Frank Kingdon Ward (1885–1958) who is best remembered for the introduction of the blue Himalayan poppy (*Meconopsis betonicifolia*). However, planthunting still continues albeit with much less adventure. The best known of today's planthunters is Roy Lancaster whose interest in plant exploration has taken him to every continent including participation in expeditions to Nepal and Yunnan, China. Bleddyn and Sue Wynn-Jones from Crug Farm Plants in North Wales also are getting a reputation as planthunters. They are the only collectors in England and Wales, other than Kew Gardens, to hold a permanent collecting licence. Every October since 1991 they have traded their home comforts for life in a tent in some remote or inhospitable part of the world. Their collecting record now equals some of the great Victorian planthunters and, as with their forebears, there still is the occasional excitement: once they ran into some poppy harvesters in the Golden Triangle. The spirit of *Boy's Own Paper* lives on!

Say It With Flowers

Today, if we wish to thank someone for their special efforts then it is customary to give them a bouquet of flowers. If we choose the selection of flowers ourselves, rather than letting the florist do it for us, we tend to select plant varieties and colours for their aesthetic appeal or because we know that they are favourites of the recipient. Other than for special occasions such as weddings and funerals we tend not to give much thought to the meaning of the flowers that we present. For example, a manager might delight his personal assistant by giving her a bunch of stargazer lilies on her birthday. But what would she think if she knew that this means 'I see heaven in your eyes'? More to the point, just think about the office gossip!

Subtlety is not a part of modern communication so knowledge of the meaning of flowers has largely been lost. However, poets and artists have always used flowers as images for feelings and as a way of expressing sentiments. Shakespeare was one of the greatest exponents of floral symbolism and his plays are full of references to plants. Consider the play *Hamlet* where Ophelia makes a speech to the royal court following the death of her father.

Ophelia (to her brother Laertes):
There's rosemary, that's for remembrance. Pray you love, remember.
And there is pansies, that's for thoughts.

Ophelia (to the King and Queen):
There's fennel for you, and columbines. There's rue for you,
And here's some for me. We call it herb of grace o' Sundays.
O, you must wear your rue with a difference! There's a daisy. I
Would give you some violets, but they wither'd all when my father died.
They say he made a good end.

Laertes was out of the country when his father died and Ophelia's message to him is very clear: she wants her brother to help her figure out who killed their father. Ophelia's message to the King and Queen is more interesting. The audience in Shakespeare's time would have known that fennel is symbolic of flattery and columbine (*Aquilegia*) of male adultery and ingratitude. Given the power of the King to take her life, Ophelia was very brave to first flatter the King and then accuse him of adultery. Rue was a major cause of abortion and thus was symbolic of female adultery (on the Queen's part) and everlasting suffering (Ophelia). Ophelia then picks up a daisy, looks at it and then puts it down. The message is clear: there is no innocence here. Finally, sweet violets (*Viola odorata*) are the symbol for faithfulness and fidelity and so Ophelia is telling the King and Queen that they lack integrity.

The floral symbolism used by Shakespeare is a powerful part of the story but present day audiences know nothing about it and so, in the case of Ophelia's speech, miss much of the drama that it contains. They fail to understand how confrontational and brave Ophelia was. Actresses playing the part of Ophelia also need an appreciation of the symbolism. A lack of knowledge of the language of flowers also can impact our appreciation of works of art. For example, in the Tate Gallery in London there is a haunting painting by Sir John Millais. It depicts Ophelia, who has drowned herself following her rejection by Hamlet. The flowers present in the painting include roses (love, youth, beauty), violets (faithfulness), forget-me-nots (remembrance), pansies (thoughts and memories) and a field poppy (everlasting sleep, death) and Ophelia is lying in the water underneath a willow tree (grief). Clearly, these flowers were not chosen by Millais at random.

Although the language of flowers largely has been lost, there are a few flowers whose symbolism is still understood. First and foremost among these is the rose. Although the rose always is associated with love, the colour of the roses and their number are very important. A single red rose means love at first sight or 'I still love you', whereas a dozen of the same colour implores 'Be mine'! A single white rose is more subtle since it is asking the recipient if they will love them. Yellow roses, on the other hand, signify dying love, infidelity or jealousy so pity the poor lover who gives them to the object of his affections. A mixture of red and white roses, or a posy of a striped rose such as Rosa Mundi, signifies a request for togetherness or unity in reference to the end of the War of the Roses. Supposedly, a gift of 999 red roses means 'I will love you till the end of time' but the unspoken message must be 'but I will be living in penury'.

Another flower that still is imbued with symbolism is the lily but, once again, colour is very important. White lilies represent purity, chastity, innocence and modesty whilst pink lilies represent romance and talent. On the other hand, yellow lilies represent falsehood and living only for the moment and day lilies (*Hemerocallis*) symbolize coquetry and short-term convenience. The lily is often to be found carved on tombstones because it represents the restoration of innocence on death and there may be added symbolism by showing a broken stem.

Should you be considering giving someone a gift of flowers you might like to consider the meaning of some of the more common varieties:

Asters	Symbol of love
Carnations (solid colour)	Adoration, fascination, remembrance
Carnations (striped)	Refusal, sorry I cannot be with you
Chrysanthemums	You are a wonderful friend
Daffodils	Regard, unrequited love

Gladioli	Strength of character
Irises	Friendship means so much
Orchids	Love, beauty and refinement

However, you should think carefully before giving dahlias (fickleness), geraniums (stupidity, folly), or *Philadelphus* (deceit). Perhaps a box of chocolates would be safer!

Drugs From Plants

Nature's Medicine Cabinet

It has been estimated by the World Health Organization that 75–80 per cent of the world's population uses medicines derived from plants, mostly in the form of herbal remedies. The vast majority do so out of necessity for they cannot afford the high cost of drugs produced by pharmaceutical companies. However, somewhat surprising, increasing numbers of consumers in developed countries such as the United States and the member states of the European Union are turning to herbal medicines. Why should this be? The most commonly cited reason is the belief that medicines derived from plants are much safer than chemically synthesized drugs.

There are herbal remedies associated with every tribe and every ethnic group on every continent. These would have been developed within early hunter-gatherer groups following trial and error experimentation with plants from their locality. Whenever beneficial results were obtained the knowledge would have been distributed by word of mouth from generation to generation. As the amount of knowledge about the medicinal properties of plants increased a person within each tribe would have been appointed as the keeper of it, the so-called 'witch doctor', 'medicine man' or 'shaman'. These individuals were, and still are, very powerful and influential and in many instances practise a heady mixture of folk medicine and religion.

The first written records of the medicinal uses of plants that we know of are from China (2700 BCE) and India (*Rig Veda*, 1500 BCE). Although the Old Testament (– 1500 BCE) is considered to be a religious text it does contain references to a number of medicaments. For example, there are frequent references to myrrh and frankincense. Although Westerners immediately think of these two substances in the context of the Three Wise Men and the birth of Jesus, in the Middle East and China they were used to treat ailments. Both substances come from small trees, *Commiphora myrrha* and *Boswellia caraterii*, that are native to the areas we know today as Dhofar, Yemen and Somalia. The first dedicated Western text on plant-based medicine was *De Materia Medica*. Written in the first century by the Roman Dioscorides, it was in common use for over 1,500 years.

Many of the plant remedies recommended by Dioscorides and other early physicians such as Hippocrates and Galen were based on observations of their therapeutic success. But, at the start of the 17th century, much of this knowledge was discounted by the writings of Jakob Bohme. A master shoemaker from Gorlitz in Germany, he had a profound mystical vision in which he saw the relation between God and man. Following this vision he developed the Doctrine of Signatures. This Doctrine states that one can determine from the colour or shape of the roots, flowers and leaves of a plant, or other signatures, the plant's purpose in God's plan. Thus the leaves of *Hepatica* species resemble the liver and so should be used to treat liver complaints. Similarly, *Pulmonaria* species (lungworts) should be used to treat lung disorders. It was nearly 200 years before common sense prevailed and the key factor was the development of chemistry.

The standard techniques for extracting and purifying chemicals were developed in the 19th century and it was not long before chemists turned their hands to the isolation of the active ingredients from herbal medicines. Thus purified salicylic acid became a more potent alternative to chewing on a willow twig to ease aches and pains and pure quinine was better than a tea brewed from *Cinchona* bark for the prevention of malaria. Today there still are prescription drugs that are isolated directly from plants: digitalin to treat heart irregularities (*Digitalis lanata*), ephedrine for bronchial decongestion (*Ephedra* species), vinblastine to treat childhood leukaemia (*Vinca*) and etoposide for treating warts and skin cancers (*Podophyllum*) to name but a few. But, unlike the herbal remedies that they replace, the active ingredient is highly purified and the product is of a consistent quality.

In developed countries, physicians have available to them a huge armoury of drugs that they can prescribe for their patients. Often they will have a choice of drugs for a particular condition so that if one particular drug does not work well there are alternatives. Consequently, certain cancers apart, there are very few conditions for which there is no effective therapy. Given this, it might come as a surprise to learn that the use of herbal remedies is booming in developed countries. In the US alone, herbal remedies are worth $3 billion (yes, billion) and are taken by an estimated 60 million people. This growth in the use of herbal medicine is of concern for two reasons: consumer safety and plant conservation.

Many westerners believe that drugs extracted from plants are safer than drugs that are chemically- synthesized. When challenged to provide the basis for this idea they usually respond that herbal remedies are free of chemicals. What do they think plants are made from? The terms 'medicine', 'drug' and 'poison' can apply to a single substance from a plant. At one concentration it can be curative, at another addictive and lethal at a higher concentration. More important, the safety and efficacy of an herbal medicine depends on the species or cultivar from which it is extracted, where the plant was grown and the weather during the growing season. Many people are convinced that *Echinacea* extracts stimulate the body's defences against viral infections but properly-conducted clinical trials have failed to demonstrate a beneficial effect. One explanation for this disappointing result is that extracts of the wrong species were used but if this is the case then ineffective remedies are on sale!

Observant gardeners will have noted that the performance of a perennial plant can vary from one year to another and a key factor in this variation is the weather. A plant that likes hot, dry weather will under-perform in a cool, wet summer, and vice versa. Similarly, the weather influences the drug content of an herbal plant. Ideally, an herbal medicine should be sold on the basis of its content of drug rather than on the weight of plant material. Even this is not a guarantee of safety for the other substances will be present in variable amounts and some of them may be at toxic levels. Many women take preparations of the black cohosh (*Actaea racemosa*) to alleviate the symptoms associated with the menopause and most have found it of benefit. However, safety of the black cohosh has not been properly assessed. The drug is known to have caused acute liver failure in a few and their only salvation was a liver transplant. There also is evidence that it may increase the spread of breast cancer. Similarly, some people taking extracts of St John's Wort (*Hypericum*) have discovered that their skin is hypersensitive to burning on exposure to strong sunlight. Caveat emptor!

The two largest users of medicinal plants are China and India. Both also have a flourishing export trade that is valued in billions of US dollars. This boom is depleting many plant species from the wild bringing some of them close to extinction. Over 80 per cent of the species used in China and 95 per cent used in India are not cultivated and Plantlife International believes that 4,000–10,000 species used in medicine are at risk. Even developed countries are not immune to the problem. In the US, at least 175 plants are collected from the wild for use in herbal medicines, including over 60 million goldenseal (*Hydrastis canadensis*) plants and 30 million ginseng plants annually. The pharmaceutical industry comes in for a lot of criticism but in the case of plant-derived medicines it always uses farmed material. The herbal medicine producers have an obligation to use sustainable sources as well.

Why Do Witches Use Broomsticks To Fly

Most of us at some time or other have seen pictures of witches flying through the air on a broomstick, often silhouetted against the moon and sometimes with a black cat for company. Those of you who have read the Harry Potter series of books will recall that broomsticks still are one of the most popular forms of transport for wizards and witches in the stories by J K Rowling. But, what was so special about broomsticks and were they really necessary for a witch to fly? The answer to these questions is linked to the use of mixtures of plant extracts as 'flying ointments'. The cats, by the way, were purely incidental to the flying process. Cats are supposed to have the ability to sense the presence of spirits before humans and black ones could remain unseen in dark places, two useful attributes as far as a witch is concerned.

Anyone trawling through the literature of witchcraft will come across many different variations of the formulae for flying ointment. Typical examples are:

Parsley, water of aconite, poplar leaves and soot
Water parsnip, sweet flag, cinquefoil, bat's blood, deadly nightshade, oil
Baby's fat, water parsnip, aconite, cinquefoil, deadly nightshade, soot

These recipes show that witches had a good knowledge of poisons as *Aconitum* (monkshood, wolfbane) and deadly nightshade (*Atropa belladonna*) are two of the most poisonous plants growing in Europe. The parsnip referred to in formula 1 may indeed be the herb used widely as a garnish today but more probably is its close relative hemlock (both are members of the family Apiaceae). Water parsnip almost certainly is cowbane, a relative of hemlock that has a thick root similar to that of the edible parsnip. The other components such as soot and bat's blood have no pharmacological effects and were probably added to enhance the mystique of the mixtures.

Deadly nightshade contains atropine, an important but very toxic drug. Atropine gets its name from Atropos, one of the three Fates of Greek mythology who chose how a person was to die. The best known use of atropine is in ophthalmology for dilation of the pupils of the eyes. Cleopatra supposedly used it for this purpose so that she would appear more alluring as did women during the Renaissance (*belladonna* is Italian for beautiful lady). If taken internally at non-fatal doses atropine will cause confusion, hallucinations and excitation.

Aconite, as extracts of *Aconitum* are known, was one of the best-known poisons of ancient times. Indeed, it was used so extensively by professional poisoners in Rome during the Empire that a law was passed making its cultivation a capital offence. At low doses aconite causes slowing and irregularity of the heart. Irregular action of the heart in a person falling asleep produces the sensation of suddenly falling through space and this may be relevant to the use of aconite in flying ointments.

Hemlock is the common name for the plant *Conium maculatum* as well as the name given to the poison extracted from it. Hemlock was the poison that Socrates drank after he was condemned to death. At toxic doses the effects of hemlock are a gradual paralysis with consciousness being unimpaired but at lower doses it can cause delirium and excitement. Water hemlock, botanical name *Cicuta virosa*, contains a drug that stimulates the central nervous system.

There is no doubt that combinations of these drugs in the form of plant extracts, especially if administered at the right dose, would have significant physiological effects that probably equated to a hallucinogenic trip. So, what role do the broomsticks play? The answer is simple: they were a drug delivery device. None of these drugs is absorbed readily through the skin and mixtures of the relevant plant extracts would be too foul tasting to drink. Therefore, witches mixed the extracts with animal fats or vegetable oils and smeared them on a broomstick. If they then sat on the broomstick the mixture would come in contact with the mucous membranes of the female pudenda (otherwise known as the 'naughty bits'!). These membranes are well supplied with blood vessels and absorption of the drugs would be rapid and lead to 'lift off'. Harry Potter and his friends at Hogwarts used Nimbus broomsticks when playing the magical game of Quidditch and propulsion was achieved without the use of flying ointment. Maybe they were smoking something behind the bicycle sheds!

The Story Of Lily The Pink

In the late 60s the British pop group The Scaffold had an unlikely hit with their song *Lily the Pink* whose chorus goes:

'We'll drink a drink a drink
To Lily the Pink the Pink the Pink
The saviour of the human race
For she invented medicinal compound
Most efficacious in every case'

This song was a sanitized version of an old folk song and most people assumed that it was no more than a children's song. However, the song is based loosely on an American entrepreneur Lydia E. Pinkham (1819–1883) whose Vegetable Compound was one of the best known patent medicines of the 19th century. Lydia Pinkham first began selling home remedies after the near bankruptcy of her husband and she went on to become the first American millonairess. Like all successful products, her Vegetable Compound satisfied an unmet market need. When it was launched in 1875 women were poorly served by the medical establishment and so it was targeted specifically at female problems such as PMT and menopausal distress.

The original formula for Lydia Pinkham's Vegetable Compound was:

Unicorn root (*Aletris farinosa*)
Life root (*Senecio aureus*)
Black cohosh (*Actaea racemosa*, formerly *Cimicifuga racemosa*)
Pleurisy root (*Asclepias tuberosa*)
Fenugreek seed (*Trigonella foenum-graecum*)
Alcohol

At least three of these plants (black cohosh, pleurisy root and life root) were used by Native Americans to treat various female complaints and it is highly likely that Lydia Pinkham simply combined them on the assumption that more is better.

According to herbalists, unicorn root provides a tonic influence on the female generative organs especially in cases of habitual miscarriage. Life root was used by Native Americans to treat vaginal discharges, to speed childbirth and to induce abortion (for birth control?). Pleurisy root gets its name from its use to treat infections of the chest and upper respiratory tract where it supposedly reduces mucosal secretions. It supposedly contains compounds that mimic the female hormone oestrogen hence its use in treating uterine disorders. It is not clear why fenugreek seeds were used in the formulation. It could have been because women in harems ate the seeds in the belief that they would become more desirable. Or it could have been because Egyptian women burned the seeds as incense to aid childbirth. However, would these facts be known to Lydia Pinkham in the mid-19th century? It is unlikely. Given that fenugreek seeds are rich in iron their inclusion may have been to combat iron deficiency from menstrual blood loss.

The most potent of the compounds in Lydia Pinkham's mixture undoubtedly was from the roots of the black cohosh. Although first used by the Native Americans it is widely used today by European, Chinese and Korean women to treat the problems associated with the onset of the menopause. However, the black cohosh needs to be used with care for there have been reports of liver failure associated with its use. It is worth noting that the black cohosh was known in Europe as 'bugbane' as it was used as an insect repellent. This use is reflected in its former botanical name *Cimicifuga* (*cimex* being Latin for bug and *fugare* meaning to drive away).

Lydia Pinkham was an active member of the women's temperance movement and so it is a little surprising that her Vegetable Compound contained 20 per cent alcohol by volume. In her defence she claimed that the alcohol was essential for the extraction of the active ingredients from the plants used and as a preservative. Both these claims probably are true. Nevertheless, her best sales were achieved long after her death when the US Prohibition movement was at its peak!

Today, it still is possible to buy Lydia's remedies although the formulations are somewhat different. One company sells Lydia Pinkham's Herbal Liquid Supplement whose ingredients are listed as motherwort, gentian, Jamaica dogwood, liquorice, dandelion, pleurisy root and black cohosh. Another product known as Lydia's Secret is sold as capsules containing, among other things, black cohosh and pleurisy root.

One of the verses in *Lily the Pink* may be a little worrying for female readers for it goes like this:

'Jennifer Eccles
Had terrible freckles
And the boys all called her names
But she changed with medicinal compound
And now HE joins in all their games'

However, there is no evidence of testosterone in any of the mixtures bearing Lydia's names so there should be no danger of a sex change occurring.

How To Avoid Being Poisoned By Your Relatives

Eupatorium purpureum is a plant native to the eastern United States where it is known as Joe Pye weed. Its common name does it an injustice for it is an excellent perennial for the back of the border where it will grow to 2m (6.5 ft) and never need staking. The flowers appear in late July and continue through to late October and provide late season colour for the herbaceous border. They are borne at the top of the stems and consist of domed heads made up of numerous small pinkish-purple flowers that are very attractive to bees, butterflies and moths. The large, lance-shaped leaves are green suffused with purple and these combine well with other late-season perennials such as yellow-flowered Rudbeckias or the coppery-orange blooms of *Helenium* Moorheim Beauty. A relative of *Eupatorium purpureum* is *Eupatorium cannabinum* and it may get you in trouble with the local constabulary. The specific epithet 'cannabinum' gives the reason for this: the plant resembles *Cannabis sativa* but smoking the leaves of it most certainly would leave you at ground level.

Native Americans used *Eupatorium purpureum* to eliminate infections such as typhoid through fever reduction. They introduced the plant to colonists who used it to treat malaria and other diseases that cause fever, particularly when quinine was in short supply. One explanation for the name Joe Pye weed is that it is a corruption of 'jopi', the Native American word for typhoid. The generic name '*Eupatorium*' was given in honour of Mithridates VI Eupator, King of Pontus from 120–63 BCE. Pontus is the name that was applied in ancient times to extensive tracts of land in the northeast of Asia Minor (modern Anatolia) bordering on the Black Sea.

When Mithridates VI was 11 years old his mother poisoned his father (Mithridates V) and he succeeded the throne. Initially his position was not secure so he poisoned his mother and brothers and married his sister Laodice. Despite this inauspicious start to his career, Mithridates VI went on to become a very successful soldier and one of Rome's most formidable and successful enemies. One curious legend about him is that he is supposed to have had a prodigious memory: Pliny the Elder and other historians reported that Mithridates was fluent in the languages of all the 22 countries that he eventually governed. However, this is irrelevant to our story.

The second legend about Mithridates is that he was afraid of being poisoned by his enemies (surprise, surprise!). Consequently, he sought to harden himself by taking increasing sub-lethal doses of the poisons he knew of until he was able to tolerate lethal doses, a process now known as mithridatism. He also fashioned a universal antidote, Antidotum Mithridaticum, containing 54 ingredients that is described in detail in the celebrated *De Medecina* written by the Roman encyclopedist Aulus Cornelius Celsus (25 BCE–50CE). One quote from *De Medecina* is that 'It is not cruel to inflict on a few criminals sufferings which may benefit multitudes of innocent people through all centuries'. This may be a reference to the practice of Mithridates of evaluating the performance of his universal antidote by testing it on prisoners captured during his wars against the Romans. This antidote was used for 1900 years after Mithridates' death and was known as Theriac.

In 63 BCE, Mithridates' reign came to an end. First he was betrayed by his eldest son, who committed suicide, and then his younger son led a rebellion against him. In danger of capture by Rome, he is alleged to have attempted suicide by poison. This failed because of the immunity that he had built up to poisons (you could not make this up) and he was forced to get his servant Bituitus to kill him with his sword. Given the history of poisoning in his family he did well to live until he was 60 years old.

The story of Mithridates is well represented in English literature. The story appears in Alexander Dumas' novel *The Count of Monte Cristo* and in *The Grass Crown*, the second volume in the *Masters of Rome* series by Colleen McCullough. It also is detailed in the following poem by the Latin scholar A. E. Houseman:

There was a king reined in the East
There, when kings will sit to feast,
They get their fill before they think
With poisoned meat and poisoned drink.
He gathered all the springs to birth
From the many-venomed earth,
First a little, thence to more
He sampled all her killing store;
And easy, smiling, seasoned sound,
Sate the king when healths went round.
They put arsenic in his meat
And stared aghast to watch him eat;
They poured strychnine in his cup
And shook to see him drink it up:
They shook, they stared as white's their shirt:
Them it was their poison hurt.
—I tell the tale that I heard told
Mithridates, he died old.

After all this you might be wondering how Mithridates was the inspiration for calling Joe Pye weed *Eupatorium.* One explanation is that Joe Pye was an American herbalist who recommended the use of extracts of the plant for the treatment of poisoning.

Plants For Naughty People

The Berberis family is an unlikely association of large shrubs such as *Berberis* and *Mahonia* and a large collection of low-growing herbaceous perennials. The herbaceous members include *Podophyllum*, *Jeffersonia* (named after Thomas Jefferson), *Vancouveria* (named after Captain George Vancouver who explored North West America), *Caulophyllum* and *Epimedium*. Some of them are not well known and rarely seen in gardens and some also are uncommon in the wild. However, *Epimedium* is in a class of its own. Unlike most plants, it will thrive in difficult areas such as among tree roots or at the bottom of walls and fences where there is little moisture. This reflects its natural habitat of woodland. It is tolerant of most soils and is free from pests and diseases and the lazy gardener will appreciate that it makes an excellent ground cover and weed suppressant.

There is much more to *Epimedium* than being simply a useful plant for an awkward spot. First of all, the new foliage as it unfolds entrances with its wide range of delicate greens and has a translucent tenderness unmatched by any other genus. Better still, *Epimedium* species have very elaborate cup-shaped or saucer-shaped flowers in which the petals have large spurs so that they resemble small aquilegias or a bishop's mitre. In recent years there has been an influx of exciting new species and varieties with fascinating colour combinations. For example, *E. acuminatum* has elegant flowers with petals and sepals in shades of lilac and purple and *E. grandiflorum* 'Freya' has deep violet flowers highlighted by white-spurred petals. Some of the newer introductions will flower for months: what more could a gardener want?

The name '*epimedium*' is a combination of two words: *epi* = upon, and *Media* = the country of the Medes (south-west of the Caspian Sea) and was first used by the Greek herbalist Dioscorides. Strangely, the plant that he described had no flowers. The herbalist John Gerard (1545–1612) gave *Epimedium* the name Barrenwort '...not because Dioscorides saith it is barren both of floures and seeds, but because being drunke it is an enemie to conception'. John Parkinson (1567–1650), who was herbalist to King James I, also made claims that powdered roots and leaves would act as a contraceptive. But, he said, the special virtue of *E.alpinum* was '...to keepe womens breasts from growing over great, being made into a cataphasme, with oyle and applied thereto...' What would he have made of the current trend for breast enhancement?

Many species of *Epimedium* are reported to have aphrodisiac properties. According to legend, this property was discovered by a Chinese goat herder who noticed excessive sexual activity in his flock after they ate the plant. In the herbal produced by Chinese Emperor Sheng Nung (see also Camellia) it is described as 'Yinyanghuo' meaning licentious goat herb. Chinese scientists have isolated a compound called icariin from *Epimedium* and have shown that its mechanism of action is exactly the same as that of Viagra. The choice of the name icariin presumably derives from the common Japanese name for *E. grandiflorum*: ikari-gusa (*ikari* = claw, *gusa* = plant), referring to the four-clawed anchor used by fishing boats which resembles the spurred flowers. Although icariin is not available as a drug, extracts of *Epimedium* are available as 'health supplements'. One well-known brand is sold under the trade name 'Horny Goatweed' and supposedly works on both men and women. It contains extracts of *E. saggitatum* and two other plants with reputations as aphrodisiacs: ginseng and Ginkgo. This product can be bought openly in Australia and the US but has been banned in the UK (spoilsports!) because medical claims are made for it.

In most of the old herbalist literature, particular plants have more than one use and *Epimedium* is no exception. The Chinese have used it to remedy absent-mindedness, to treat corneal infections, to slow down bone loss in osteoporosis, to reduce fatigue and stress and to treat breast cancer. They also used it to treat sterility and barrenness in women – the opposite of the use recommended by John Gerard! One explanation might be that the Chinese thought that sterility was nothing more than loss of sexual appetite. There is an alternative explanation. *Epimedium* contains at least 15 pharmacologically active compounds and the way in which the plant is processed will influence what is present and in what quantities. The Chinese would have taken *Epimedium* as a hot water decoction (a tea) whereas Gerard and Parkinson recommended powdered root and leaves or an alcoholic (wine) extract.

Caulophyllum is a genus of one species (*C. thalictroides*) with two varieties growing in shady woodlands: one in eastern North America and one in East Asia. The plant has a number of common names such as blue cohosh, papoose-root and squaw-root. The first name is a reference to its characteristic blue berries and the other two to its gynaecological use by Native American women. In particular, blue cohosh tea was used to relieve menstrual cramps and the pain associated with childbirth, to inducing uterine contractions to speed delivery, to stimulate delivery of a retained placenta and to stop post-natal bleeding. Use of the blue cohosh probably was beneficial for the plant has been shown to contain two substances similar to oxytocin, a hormone produced during childbirth and which causes the uterus to contract. However, there is a darker side to *Caulophyllum*: Native American women used a strong decoction as a contraceptive and if this worked it most likely was because it acted as an abortifacient. Today, blue cohosh extracts are purchased from herbal stores principally to terminate unwanted pregnancies. This raises the question; does *Epimedium* make a woman barren in the same way?

The Keys Of Paradise

The plants that most of us know as poppies belong to the genus *Papaver*. This genus consists of about 50 species of annual, biennial and perennial herbaceous plants and many are grown as ornamentals. The Iceland or Arctic poppy, *P. nudicale*, is an annual that self-seeds happily and occurs in a wide range of garish colours. The tall perennial garden poppies that have flowers in colours of orange, pink, white and red are oriental poppies (*P. orientale*).The field poppy, *P. rhoeas*, has blood red flowers and grows vigorously in newly-turned soil. Because of its association with the poem *In Flanders Fields* it is known also as the Remembrance poppy. In 1880, the Reverend William Wilks noticed an unusual field poppy growing in a field. He collected the seed and used it to propagate what became known as the 'Shirley Poppy'. Today, there are a whole series of Shirley poppies and the original one is named after its originator. Wilks went on to become Secretary of the Royal Horticultural Society where he established the annual show that became the Chelsea Flower Show.

Petals of both *P. orientale* and *P. rhoeas* are used as a source of red dye (rhoeadine) used in wines and medicines. But the keys of paradise, as Thomas de Quincey (1785–1859) called them, come from yet another poppy, the opium poppy (*P. somniferum*). The name of the genus, *Papaver*, comes from the Latin for milk and is an allusion to the milk-like opium-containing latex produced by the seed pods of some species. The specific epithet *somniferum* means sleep-inducing. In Spanish the poppy is known as *adormidera* in reference to its sleep inducing properties.

Opium gatherers go into poppy fields at sunset a few days after the petals fall. They make horizontal incisions in the unripe poppy-heads or capsules and over the next 24 hours a milky latex (opium, from the Greek *opos* meaning juice)) bleeds from the cuts. This latex is collected and either formed into cakes for sale or processed into narcotics. These narcotics belong to a class of chemicals known as alkaloids and the most powerful one in opium poppies is morphine. The great benefit of morphine is that it abolishes pain without inducing loss of consciousness but regular use leads to dependency. Another alkaloid found in poppies is codeine. It has one seventh the biological activity of morphine but is more orally active and less likely to lead to addiction. Heroin is produced chemically from morphine and initially was considered to be safer than morphine but now is known to be the most addictive drug used in medicine.

There is much evidence that the opium poppy is native to the countries surrounding the Mediterranean Sea. Intact capsules of *P. somniferum* that date to 5500 BCE have been found in a cave in southern Spain and Egyptian hieroglyphics from 4000 BCE record mothers giving crying children poppy heads to suck. References to the poppy can be found in Homer's *Iliad* and in ancient Crete there was a poppy goddess who wore a crown with three capsules. Pliny the Elder warned of the dangers of opium and the Roman Emperor Marcus Aurelius was known to be an addict.

When the Romans invaded Britain they brought many different plants with them. The opium poppy was one of these plants. Since the Romans had little use for decorative plants we can surmise that the poppy was brought for its analgesic properties. The first description of the poppy in English literature is Chaucer's reference to it in the *Knight's Tale*:

A clarree, maed of a certyn wyn
With narcotikes and opie of Thebes fyn

A clarree was a sweet liquor made of wine, clarified honey and various spices. In the 16th century the Swiss physician Paracelsus experimented with the medicinal properties of opium and concocted an alcoholic extract that he called Laudanum. In the 17th century, English physicians recommended its use for relief of pain, sleeplessness and diarrhoea. In the Victorian era it became a staple of the household medicine cabinet. As Frenchman Rene Rapin (1621–1687) put it:

> The pow'rful Seeds when press'd afford a Juice
> In Med'cine fam'd, and Sov'reign for its use;
> Whether in tedious Nights with charm to rest,
> Or bind the stubborn cough, and ease the lab'ring breast.

Initially laudanum was a drug of the working classes. Although it contained alcohol it was treated as a medication and not taxed as an alcoholic beverage. This made laudanum cheaper than a bottle of gin or wine. Laudanum became a favourite of writers and artists because it enabled them to discreetly satisfy their need for opium rather than visit opium dens. Notable literary figures that were addicted include Edgar Allan Poe, Samuel Taylor Coleridge, Thomas de Quincey (who wrote Confessions of an English Opium Eater), Lord Byron, Percy Bysshe Shelley, Elizabeth Barrett Browning, John Keats and Charles Darwin. William Wilberforce who helped abolish slavery also was a user.

In the 1790s the London Society of Arts encouraged the growing of pharmaceutical plants and offered cash prizes to successful growers of opium poppies. One winner was John Ball of Somerset who grew a bumper crop. This came to the attention of farmers in Mitcham in Surrey and by 1830 the town had become the opium capital of Britain. Opium fell out of favour at the end of the 19th century because of growing concerns about its psychotropic effects and addictive properties. The introduction of the 1920 Dangerous Drugs Act in the UK, and similar legislation in other countries, made it illegal to possess opium without a doctor's prescription.

Today, opium poppies are grown legally in a small number of countries: Australia, Japan and India and only India exports opium for pharmaceutical use. About 40 per cent of the legally traded opiates are manufactured in Tasmania, Australia from locally grown poppies. Recently there has been a world shortage of legally produced opium poppies and they have been cultivated again in Britain. One newspaper carried a picture of opium poppies growing at a 'secret location' in England. This showed a large field of poppies in flower dominated by a well-known power station!

When poppies are grown for seed production for decoration of bread, the crop is harvested when the capsules turn yellow green and the seed rattles in them. The seeds are not narcotic but should you be foolish enough to want the keys to paradise then all you have to do is sow some of the seeds in your garden and wait for the poppies to grow and flower.

Artemisias, Absinthe And Anti-Malarials

Artemisia is a genus of the daisy family that is named after Artemis, the Greek goddess of hunting and fertility. The genus contains about 300 species of evergreen and deciduous shrubs, perennials and annuals. In the garden they are grown mostly for their foliage, as the flowers are not particularly attractive, with the exception of *Artemisia dracunculus* (Tarragon) whose leaves are used for seasoning. Artemisias generally have a pungent odour that is a mix of citrus and camphor and some varieties are used as sources of fragrances for men. In earlier times they were used to keep moths from clothes and as a flea repellent.

There is much folklore associated with artemisias. *A. abrotanum* has many common names including southernwood, lad's love, maiden's ruin, and kiss in my corner. The origin of these names is lost in the mists of time but almost certainly have a connection with courtship. In the Cambridgeshire Fens, young men would carry a sprig of the plant and offer it to the village girls. Any girl who accepted it would be invited for a romantic stroll. There are many stories of incredible, and sometimes erotic, dreams after southernwood was placed in pillows or hung above the bed. The plant is also reputed to be an aphrodisiac. If *Artemisia* really has these properties then the common names will come as no surprise. The surprise is that the plant was named after Artemis as she also was the goddess of virginity!

Artemisia absinthium, also known as wormwood, apparently sprung up in the trail of the Devil as he left the Garden of Eden. Modern day devils, in the form of Italian drivers, tie some wormwood to their windscreens before driving on precipitous roads. One can only imagine that the practice increases their daredevil behaviour. A more prosaic use for wormwood, and its relative *A. ponticus* (Roman wormwood), is in the provision of the flavouring for absinthe and vermouth. To make absinthe, wormwood first is macerated in alcohol along with fennel and aniseed, a process that releases the very bitter substance absinthine. The extract then is distilled to produce a colourless liquid. In the manufacture of traditional absinthe, herbs are added and this results in a green colour as the alcohol releases chlorophyll from the plant tissues. Finally, water is added to give the desired percentage of alcohol. Over time, and with exposure to light, the chlorophyll breaks down changing the colour of the absinthe from emerald green to yellow-green and then amber.

The precise origin of absinthe is unclear but in the late 18th century it was being sold in Switzerland as a medicinal elixir. In 1797, the formula was purchased by a Major Dubied, his son Marcellin and son-in-law Henry-Louis Pernod. They opened their first distillery in Switzerland under the name Dubied Pere et Fils. In 1805 they opened their second absinthe distillery in Pontarlier, France under the name Maison Pernod Fils. Eventually other companies started producing absinthe but the name Pernod became synonymous with the drink.

In the mid-19th century the French government gave absinthe to its troops as a fever preventative. When the troops returned home they brought their taste for absinthe with them and it became popular in bars and bistros. Initially it was favoured mainly by the bourgeoisie and eccentric Bohemian artists but as the price dropped the market expanded until it became the drink of France. At the start of the 20th century sales in France were over 35 million litres per year but its demise was forthcoming. An unlikely coalition of the temperance movement and winemakers' associations successfully blamed absinthe for all kinds of social ills and high profile crimes. With the exception of Spain, countries around the world banned the sale of absinthe and France finally followed suit in 1915.

The effects of absinthe have been described by habitués as mind-opening and even hallucinogenic and the drink was popular with artists and writers such as Oscar Wilde, Pablo Picasso, Toulouse Lautrec, Edouard Manet and Edgar Allan Poe. On the other hand, the prohibitionists claimed it turned good people 'mad and desolate'. In support of this view they cited Edgar Degas' painting *L'Absinthe* that features two bored-looking individuals – despite the fact that this scene could equally have been painted in an English teashop of the period. Drinking too much absinthe reputedly can affect one's vision by making the colour spectrum appear mainly yellow (xanthopsia). Vincent van Gogh was known to drink absinthe heavily and this fact is used to explain the excessive use of the colour yellow in his later paintings. Absinthe is known to contain thujone, a neurotoxin that can cause xanthopsia. However, the concentration in absinthe is so low that a drinker would become unconscious from the alcohol long before developing yellow vision. An alternative explanation for van Gogh's excessive use of yellow may have been that he felt bilious. When drinking with his friend Toulouse-Lautrec his favourite cocktail was an 'Earthquake': two parts absinthe, one part red wine and a generous slug of cognac!

As noted above, French troops drank absinthe as a fever preventative and one of the fevers that they would have wanted to avoid would have been malaria. Since absinthe contains extracts of wormwood, drinking it may well have had the desired prophylactic effect. A close relative of wormwood is *Artemisia annua*, a highly aromatic annual herb native to China that has been used as a medicinal plant for over 4,000 years. In 1971 it was shown that extracts of *A. annua* were active against the malarial parasite. A year later, the active ingredient was isolated and is known as qinghaosu in China and artemisinin in the West. The significance of this discovery cannot be underestimated: malaria kills over one million people every year. Derivatives of artemisinin have been licensed as pharmaceuticals all over the world, the first drugs based on traditional Chinese medicine to achieve this status.

For treating fevers, Chinese herbalists prescribed a tea made from *A.*

annua. Undoubtedly this would have had a bitter taste, as did the absinthe drunk by French soldiers. The alternative treatment for fevers such as malaria was quinine, another intensely bitter compound only made palatable by its formulation as tonic water. Is this the origin of the idea, much favoured by mothers, that a medicine that does not taste bad will not do you any good?

Flowers For The Heart

Most people, even if they are not gardeners, can recognize the common foxglove (*Digitalis purpurea*) that grows wild in British hedgerows and woodlands and know that it is the source of a drug (digoxin) that is used to treat heart conditions. What is less commonly known is that digoxin was one of the first herbal remedies to be developed into a modern drug. The story of its development is a very interesting one.

The origin of the name 'foxglove' is not known but almost certainly is connected with stories about fairies. Some think the original name was 'folksglove', a reference to the shape of the flowers which resemble the fingers of a glove. The 'folk' were the fairies whose favourite haunts were supposed to be in woodlands where foxgloves thrive. Support for this comes from a list of plants compiled at the time of Edward III (1312–1377) that includes folksgloves. Another explanation for the name is that bad fairies gave the flowers to the fox that he might put them on his toes to soften his tread when stealing chickens. The German name 'fingerhut' (thimble) suggested to the herbalist Leonard Fuchs that the plant be given the name *Digitalis* since the Latin for a thimble is *Digitabulum*.

In the Middle Ages herbalists used the foxglove for many different purposes, most of them unconnected with its modern use. Gerard recommended it for those 'who have fallen from high places'. Parkinson promoted the use of the juice of the leaves for cleaning old sores, ulcers and scrofulous swellings. Others, such as Culpepper, used it to treat wounds. Shakespeare was very knowledgeable of plants and their uses, and his son-in-law was a physician, but there is no mention in any of his plays of the foxglove.

The discovery of the true beneficial effects of foxgloves is accredited to the physician William Withering (1741–1799). Strictly speaking, he did not make the discovery; rather, he undertook the first proper clinical studies on it, albeit it in a way that would not be approved today. In 1775, Withering was asked his opinion on a folk remedy for dropsy which was a usually fatal oedema resulting from congestive heart failure. This remedy had long been kept a secret by a gipsy woman in Shropshire who sometimes cured people where physicians had failed. Withering managed to extricate from her a list of all the herbs in her remedy. Based on his botanical and medical training he suspected that the foxglove was the 'active' ingredient. Over the next 10 years, Withering experimented with the plant using different dosage regimes in order to find the best way of administering it. In his classic paper of 1785, *An Account of the Foxglove and Some of Its Medical Uses, With Practical Remarks on Dropsy and Other Diseases*, Withering confessed to years of over-medicating patients to dangerous levels with a host of painful side effects, even to the extent of causing more rapid death. Nevertheless, this was the first report of a human clinical trial of a drug.

A neighbour and friend of Withering was Erasmus Darwin, another physician and grandfather of Charles Darwin. He wrote an epic poem, *Botanic Garden*, in which he describes many of the plants of the time and their uses. In part 2 of this poem he describes the suffering of a patient with dropsy and their relief with digitalis:

Bolster'd with down, amid a thousand wants,
Pale Dropsy rears his bloated form, and pants;
'Quench me ye cool pellucid rills,' he cries,
Wets his parched tongue and rolls his hollow eyes.
So bends tormented Tantalus to drink

While from his lips the refluent waters shrink;
Again the rising stream his bosom laves
And thirst consumes him mid circumfluent waves.
Divine Hygeia from the bending sky
Descending, listens to his piercing cry;
Assumes bright Digitalis dress and air;
Her ruby check, white neck and raven hair;
Four youths protect her from the circling throng,
And like the Nymph the Goddess steps along,
O'er him she waves he serpent wreathed wand,
Cheers with her voice and raises with her hand
Warms with rekindling bloom his visage wan,
And charms the shapeless monster into man.

Another remarkable aspect of Withering was that he recognized the problems inherent in the use of plants as a source for medicines. That is, the concentration of the active substance varies greatly depending on the species or cultivar that is used, the part(s) of the plant used and the time of harvesting. Withering chose to use only the leaves of the foxglove and to harvest them when the plant was in flower so as to guarantee a defined medication. Not content with that, he would administer the extract in increasing doses until the first signs of side effects occurred and then stop treatment. Since digoxin takes a long time to be eliminated from the body the therapeutic effects would occur for weeks after treatment was stopped. One hundred years after Wittering began his studies on foxgloves, a German chemist called Oswald Schmiedeberg isolated the active drug substance and called it digitoxin.

Withering became one of the most successful doctors outside of London and by the time he was 46 was renting the handsome Edgbaston Hall outside Birmingham. This boasted one of the first water closets in the area! In later life he investigated the phenomenon of fairy rings and discovered that they were caused by mushrooms. He died of tuberculosis in 1799 and is buried at Edgbaston Old Church where his memorial is decorated with foxgloves. There is a certain irony in the cause of his death for foxgloves belong to the family Scrophulariaceae. The name is derived from scrofula, a form of tuberculosis, because several species of *Scrophularia* have been used to treat the disease.

The use of foxgloves to treat dropsy turns up in George Eliot's novel *Silas Marner*. In the novel, Marner is taking a pair of shoes to be mended when he sees the cobbler's wife, Sally Oates, seated by the fire and suffering from the terrible effects of dropsy. Recalling the relief that his mother had found from a simple preparation of foxglove, Marner promises to bring Sally something that will ease her plight. This he does and he 'made her sleep like a baby, when her heart had been beating enough to burst her body, for two months and more, while she had been under the doctor's care'. However, Silas Marner's supposed knowledge is an anachronism. Although the story was written in 1861 it is set in 1810 and Marner's mother is already dead. It is unlikely then that his mother could have known of the beneficial effects of foxglove given that Withering only published his treatise in 1785.

Agatha Christie was well aware of the toxicity of the foxglove, and the similarity of the leaves to those of sage, for she incorporated it into the plot of her murder mystery *The Herb of Death*. The story revolves around the apparent accidental poisoning of the guests of Sir Ambrose Bercy after they had consumed roast duck with sage and onion stuffing. It develops that foxgloves were growing alongside the sage and the leaves of both were collected and presented to the cook. When one of the dinner guests dies the amateur sleuth Miss Marple deduces that the victim was given an overdose of digitalis and that the food poisoning was cleverly engineered to disguise this fact. Christie also made use of foxglove leaves as a poison in her very last novel, *Postern of Fate*.

The makers of the 2006 movie *Casino Royale*, in a major deviation from the original Ian Fleming script, incorporate a scene where James Bond nearly dies from cardiac arrest when his drink is spiked with digoxin. Thanks to the power of computerized diagnostics, Bond quickly finds out what has been used to poison him and a shot of lignocaine plus a jolt from a defibrillator means that he can immediately return to the gambling tables. Of course, there was no real danger of Bond 'Withering away'…!

The Science Of Scent And Colour

Making Sense Of Scents

Every plant synthesizes thousands of different chemical compounds and we are oblivious to most of them. However, a small number of these compounds evaporate easily into the atmosphere, i.e. they are volatile, and this means that we can smell them. These scents range from the sensual perfume of roses through the pungent bite of cloves to the putrid smell of rotting flesh emitted by the Dragon Arum (*Dracunculus vulgaris*). But, given that a plant has to expend energy to make these scents why does it bother to do so? There are two basic reasons why plants make scents: pollination and protection.

Many flowering plants rely on insects to transfer their pollen so that seeds can be produced but how do you tell an insect where you are? One way is to produce brightly-coloured flowers. Another is to communicate by smell. Insects have a vast array of scent receptors on their antennae and these can detect scent molecules when present at only a few parts per billion. Consequently, they can find a perfumed flower from quite some distance away. Nature is never wasteful and so it should come as no surprise that, in general, the brightest coloured flowers have the least scent and vice versa. Thus, white flowers tend to smell the strongest followed by pale yellow, pale pink and mauve-pink.

Given that it takes energy to make scent there is no point in wasting it and so flowers tend to make scents when the chances are greatest that their insect pollinators will be around. The body temperature of an insect is that of the surrounding air: think of a butterfly that closes its wings when the sun goes behind a cloud. Thus flowers smell most strongly on warm sunny days when insects will be out and about. As the temperature rises during a sunny day, more and more of the scent will volatilize and the aroma will spread over a wider and wider area. Not surprisingly, rose petals used for making attar of roses are harvested in the early morning before the scent has had time to evaporate. Flowers do not need to be pollinated until they are fully opened and so do not produce their scent whilst still in bud. Similarly, flowers stop making scent after being pollinated.

Some flowers are pollinated by night-flying insects such as nocturnal moths. It would be pointless for these flowers to make scent during the day when their pollinating insects are not about. Consequently they produce their scent after dark and the scent is strongest on warm, still summer nights when flying conditions for the moths are at their best. Some plants that are pollinated at night even go so far as to close up their flowers during the day. One such plant is *Mirabilis jalapa* (the 4-o-clock plant). It opens its flowers in the late afternoon and keeps them open all night and closes them as the sun comes up.

If a plant has scented flowers then the function of the fragrance is the attraction of insects for the purposes of pollination. However, if a plant has aromatic leaves then the role of the volatile chemicals produced is protection. This protection takes a number of forms. Many plants with aromatic leaves grow in hot environments such as the countries bordering the Mediterranean. The oily vapour produced by these plants increases as the temperature rises and provides protection from the scorching effects of the sunshine. It does this in two ways. First, it filters out much of the ultra-violet irradiation in the same way as sun-blockers used by humans. Second, it takes a lot of energy (latent heat) to convert a liquid into a vapour. Just as the evaporation of sweat cools us down on a hot day so too does the evaporation of volatile substances from the surface of leaves. This can be turned to good effect by house owners in hot countries. Planting rosemary, thyme and lavender close to a house will reduce the heat adsorbed by the walls.

Many aromatic plants, such as herbs, produce their fragrant oils in special storage cells below the leaf surface. As a consequence their fragrance is not produced until the leaf is rubbed or crushed. The reason for this is simple. The function of the fragrance is protection and there is no point in releasing it until attacked. Some of these protective fragrances may smell attractive to us, e.g. rosemary, but the vast majority are very unpleasant and will discourage herbivores tempted to eat them: just think of the foetid smell of crushed leaves of *Clerodendron* species! Some plants have evolved an even more dramatic use of scents for protective purposes: they attract the enemies of their predators. For example, corn plants emit a particular cocktail of scents when they are attacked by certain pests such as the caterpillar known as the Egyptian cotton leaf worm. Parasitic wasps use the plant scent to localize the caterpillars so that they can deposit their eggs on them. As the eggs hatch, the larvae consume the caterpillar and the plant is relieved from its attacker. At least 15 species of plant are known to use this defence which gives new meaning to the old phrase 'the enemy of my enemy is my friend'.

The insect-repellent properties of plant oils have been used by man for centuries, particularly lavender oil and oil of citronella. The latter is particularly useful in that it is repellent to an extremely wide selection of insects including ants, beetles, cockroaches, fleas, flies, mites, mosquitoes, moths, ticks and wasps. Unfortunately, it smells 'cheap and nasty' (I still can remember breaking a gallon bottle of it in the chemist's shop where I worked as a teenager). Fortunately, scientists have discovered that many other plant oils can be used as alternatives to citronella even if they do not have its breadth of activity. Thus the oils from cinnamon, eucalyptus, geranium, pennyroyal, sandalwood and the tea tree will repel mosquitoes but only those from cinnamon and pennyroyal will repel ticks. Nevertheless, perfumers now can formulate new floral scents that are appealing to the human nose whilst repelling a selected panel of insects.

Just as plants make scents that will attract pollinating insects, so humans use fragrances to attract the opposite sex with reproduction as the ultimate goal. Also like plants, humans only use these fragrances when the person of their interest is likely to be present! The use of plant-derived perfumes is believed to have started with the ancient Persians. Since most of their early literature was destroyed by invaders it is not known if they wrote down their fragrance formulae. The Egyptians certainly did and there are written records for making perfume that are 2,500–5,000 years old. The practice of perfumery was further refined by the Romans and the word 'perfume' is derived from the Latin '*per fume*' meaning *through smoke*. These early perfumes were mixtures of olive oil and crushed petals or herbs until the Arabian chemist Avicenna developed the process of extracting oils from flowers by steam distillation.

After the Fall of the Roman Empire the art of perfumery was lost from Europe and it was another 1,000 years before the skills were regained. The first perfume in a form as we know it today was created in Hungary in the 14th century for their Queen Elizabeth. Known as Hungary Water, it consisted of a blend of scented oils in alcohol. Over 300 years later, in 1709, Johann Maria Farina created the iconic *Eau de Cologne*. In the late 19th and early 20th century the London firm of Penhaligon's produced a number of famous perfumes such as English Fern but for the past 100 years the world of perfumery has been dominated by the French with names such as *No5* (Chanel 1921), *Joy* (Jean Patou 1930), *Monsieur* (Givenchy 1959), *Opium* (Yves Saint Laurent 1977) and *Poison* (Christian Dior 1985). Currently there is a trend for celebrities to sign contracts with perfume houses to associate their name with a signature scent. Examples are Victoria Beckham (*Intimately for Her*) and Naomi Campbell (*Mystery*) but the best must surely be *Moi* that is promoted by Miss Piggy from the Muppets!

Finally, for those of you who have reached a stage where remembering things is difficult, scents can be used to help your memory. If you read or hear something whilst in the vicinity of a scented flower and then forget what it was all you have to do to recall it is smell the flower again. But which flower was it …?

Lavender's Blue, Dilly Dilly

'After all these faire and sweet flowers I must need add a few sweet herbs, both to accomplish this garden and to please your sense...'

So wrote John Parkinson in 1629 when justifying why he gave lavender pride of place in his garden. Gardeners today still use lavender for the same purpose. But its history is much, much older. Over 2,500 years ago, lavender was used by the Egyptians, Phoenicians and the peoples of Arabia for perfume and in the mummification of bodies. The Romans used lavender oils for bathing, cooking and scenting the air but the plant was not cheap: flowers were sold for 100 denarii per pound, the equivalent of one month's wages for a labourer or servant. In what might have been an early marketing ploy, the Romans believed that the asp (a kind of viper) made its nest in lavender bushes thereby making harvesting difficult and driving up the price.

Lavender is mentioned frequently in the Holy Bible where it goes under the name of spikenard. In the gospel according to Luke there is a description of Mary anointing the feet of Jesus with ointment of spikenard. It is not clear when the plant got its current name of lavender but the Romans may have derived the name from either of the Latin roots, *lavare* meaning to wash or *livendula* meaning bluish. In medieval times the washing women were known as lavenders. When Linnaeus Latinized plant names he put lavender in the genus *Lavandula.*

The genus *Lavandula* contains some 30 species and an unknown number of garden varieties. Producers of lavender oil recognize three types: fine lavender, spike lavender and lavandine. Fine lavender types include *L. angustifolia*, *L. vera* and *L. officinalis*, all of them small plants with a single flower on each stem. The oil from fine lavenders has medicinal properties and is much sought after by perfume manufacturers. Spike lavender (*L. latifolia* and *L. spica*) are tall plants with several branches and each stem carries several small flowers. The oil from spike lavenders has a strong camphor smell and is not used to make perfume. Lavandine (*L.x intermedia*) is a sterile hybrid created by crossing a spike lavender with a fine lavender. It has much higher oil content than fine lavender but the oil does not have the medicinal qualities of that from fine lavender and the scent lacks subtlety.

There are many medicinal claims for lavender oil. It is known to be a potent antimicrobial agent and has been used, albeit incorrectly, for centuries to prevent disease. In 16th century France the glove-makers of Grasse scented their leather with lavender oil and supposedly resisted cholera – despite cholera being caught from contaminated water! During the Great Plague in London in the 17th century it was suggested that a bunch of lavender fastened to each wrist would protect the wearer against the deadly disease. In this case the effect of the lavender would be to repel the fleas that spread the disease. During the Black Death in the 14th century a group of thieves who robbed dead victims of the disease purportedly survived because they washed in Four Thieves Vinegar. Since this concoction included vinegar, garlic, and other herbs in addition to lavender it is not surprising that fleas and other insects kept their distance. Four Thieves Vinegar found favour again in 1793 in Philadelphia when there was an outbreak of yellow fever, another disease transmitted by insects.

Lavender oil has been used with success to treat a variety of skin conditions including minor skin infections, acne and thrush. In Edward Lear's humorous poem *The Pobble Who Has No Toes* there is a verse that goes:

'His Aunt Jobiska made him drink
Lavender water tinged with pink,
For she said 'The world in general knows
There's nothing so good for a Pobble's toes'

This might be thought of as a reference to the known anti-fungal properties of lavender oil. However, lavender water is made by steeping lavender flowers in strong alcoholic beverages so the effect more likely is one of light-headedness.

Lavender is widely used by aromatherapists and herbalists but clinical studies only have demonstrated a genuine benefit for insomnia and stress. In folklore, pillows were filled with lavender to help the restless fall asleep and Charles VI of France supposedly demanded such pillows wherever he went. This use of lavender is described by John Keats in his poem about a girl who could see her future husband in a dream if she performed certain rites on the eve of St Agnes:

'And still she slept an azure-lidded sleep,
In blanched linen, smooth and lavender'd'

Today, many people put a few drops of lavender oil on their pillows or massage it into their temples.

The calming effects of lavender make it useful for reducing stress in general and for treating headaches. In the 16th century, people used to tuck a small sachet of lavender flowers under their hats to guard against headaches. Elizabeth the First wanted fresh lavender flowers available every day of the year, a demand that must have given her gardeners stress given the English climate! Just think of the stress that she would have had if it was not available.

It is well known that the Romans washed regularly and perfumed their bodies but after the fall of the Roman Empire the bathwater was tossed away with the rest of that civilization. During Elizabethan times even royalty did not wash. Rather, they tended to use scents such as lavender to mask body odours. By the 17th century, the use of soap and water was coming back into fashion. In 1620, a man by the name of Yardley paid Charles I a large sum of money to gain a concession to manufacture soap for the whole of London. This business was maintained by successive generations and in 1770 Yardley opened its first shop in London selling luxury soap perfumed with lavender. Today, the name Yardley is synonymous with lavender as a fragrance.

Lavender and seduction have been linked since time immemorial. In some versions of the Old Testament there is a Book of Judith. This tells the story of Judith anointing herself with lavender before seducing Holofernes, the enemy commander. This allowed her to murder him and thus save the city of Jerusalem. Cleopatra also made use of lavender in the seduction of Julius Caesar and Mark Anthony and lavender was among the offerings of the Queen of Sheba to King Solomon. In the Middle Ages, lavender was put under the beds of newlyweds because it stirred the passions and this is reflected in the 17th century lullaby '*Lavender's blue dilly, dilly*' which has the words 'Whilst you and I diddle, diddle ...keep the bed warm.' Fortunately, most children will not understand the innuendo.

Nature's Deodorant

Dealers in used cars know that the odour of either cigarettes or dogs can greatly reduce the value of a car. This is because both odours are extremely difficult to eliminate and have a habit of recurring no matter how often the interior furnishings are cleaned. A few years ago I was intrigued to find in the *Daily Telegraph* a letter offering a solution to this problem. All one had to do was to cut one's grass on a dry day and put the clippings in a box on the back seat for about three weeks. If the odour still persisted after this time then the process should be repeated once more. No explanation was provided for this miraculous cure and the information was mentally filed away. It was only when I was searching for information on Sweet Woodruff that I uncovered the secret.

Sweet Woodruff (*Galium odoratum*) is a low-growing herbaceous perennial plant that does best in partial or full shade in moist soils. It is not a very striking plant, even when it produces its small white flowers in May and June. Nevertheless, it has a place in the garden on account of its ability to form a spreading, weed-suppressing mat under shrubs and trees. The plant has been given many common names including Sweetscented Bedstraw, Ladies Bedstraw, Wild Baby's Breath and Queen of the Woods. When the foliage is newly gathered it has little odour but on drying it develops a most refreshing scent of new-mown hay that is retained for years. The famous 16th century herbalist John Gerard had this to say about sweet Woodruff:

> The flowers are of a very sweet smell as is the rest of the herb, which, being made up into garlands or bundles, and hanged up in houses in the heat of summer, doth very well attemper the air, cool and make fresh the place, to the delight and comfort of such as are therein.

The agreeable odour of Sweet Woodruff, and that of new-mown hay, is due to the presence of coumarin. This chemical has two properties that make it of use to perfumers. First, it has a pleasant fragrance in its own right. Second, it has the ability to fix other odours by combining with them. To a perfumer, fixing is a desirable property because it makes the overall fragrance last longer. Fixing also makes coumarin a deodorant because it combines with volatile compounds that have an unpleasant odour thereby reducing their concentration in the air around us. Not surprisingly, coumarin is found in many proprietary deodorants on sale today.

Sweet Woodruff was widely used in Tudor houses and churches to sweeten the air. It also has been used in clothes drawers, wardrobes and library shelves to remove musty smells. The alternative common name of Ladies Bedstraw derives from its use to stuff mattresses. However, it is not clear whether its use in bedding was on account of its pleasant smell and deodorant properties or its ability to repel insects. Given the lack of washing facilities in earlier times and the common occurrence of fleas and lice, the availability of Sweet Woodruff must have been a real blessing.

The Elizabethan herbalist Nicholas Culpepper recommended that the bruised leaves of Woodruff be applied to cuts and wounds as they had a healing effect. He also recommended the use of liquid extracts to stop inward bleeding, nose bleeds and obstructions of the liver. Other herbalists recommend the use of decoctions of Woodruff to eliminate kidney stones and treat urinary diseases and the French have been known to use them to treat epilepsy.

As well as being a deodorant and herbal remedy, Woodruff also finds use as a flavouring agent. In Germany it is used to flavour wine (Maiwein), beer (Berliner Weisse), brandy, sausages and jam, and to make a herbal tea with gentle sedative properties. Maiwein (May wine) is drunk in the Spring, particularly around the May Day holiday. It is made by steeping Woodruff in white German wine and adding other ingredients such as brandy, carbonated water and sugar to make a punch – hence the alternative name Maibowle (May bowl). The European Union has managed to get in on the act by ruling on a legal definition of Maiwein:

> An aromatized drink obtained from wine with added *Asperula odorata* (= *Galium odorata*) plants or extracts thereof so as to ensure a predominant taste of *Asperula odorata*. So now you know!

If you grow *Galium odorata* in your garden and want to use it as a flavouring agent with a difference then a quick search on the internet will produce a wide range of recipes. A better use might be to stuff a bunch of leaves into all the smelly footware in your shoe cupboard or under the blanket in your dog's basket!

The Search For The Blue Rose And The Black Tulip

There are three reasons why we might grow a particular flowering plant in our garden: shape, scent and colour. Of these three, colour is by far the most important for it is the only one that has the same impact close up and at a distance. In planning an herbaceous border we try to select plants with complementary colours so that the overall visual effect is a pleasing one. For all sorts of reasons, most of us also have a preference for certain genera of plants and we will seek out new varieties with novel colour, shape, and growth habit combinations. But, in many cases, the variation that occurs naturally does not vary beyond certain bounds. For example, *Geranium* species have flowers that are pink, blue, purple and white but never yellow or orange. Why should this be? Similarly, why has nobody found a blue rose and why is black such an elusive colour?

The colour that we see in flowers comes from various pigments and there are three basic types. The presence of anthocyanidins gives flowers red, purple and blue colours. Examples are the scarlet 'pelargonidin' from *Pelargonium*, the purple 'petunidin' from *Petunia* and the blue-violet 'delphinidin' from *Delphinium*. By contrast, the pigments known as carotenes give yellow, orange and red-coloured flowers. Another group known as flavones are responsible for pale yellow colours. The synthesis of these different pigments involves many biochemical reactions and each reaction is under the control of a separate gene. If a plant lacks the relevant genes for the synthesis of a particular pigment then the flower will never make the pigment. Carnations and roses lack the genes for making the blue pigment delphinidin and no matter how hard we search we will not find blue carnations or blue roses occurring naturally. According to Rudyard Kipling:

Roses red and roses white
Plucked I for my love's delight.
She would none of all my posies-
Bade me gather her blue roses.

Half the world I wandered through,
Seeking where such flowers grew
Half the world unto my quest
Answered me with laugh and jest.

Home I came at wintertide
But my silly love had died
Seeking with her latest breath
Roses from the arms of Death

It may be beyond the grave
She shall find what she would have
Mine was but an idle quest-
Roses white and red are best!

Although blue carnations and roses do not occur naturally a company in Australia, Florigene, has created them in the laboratory using genetic engineering. Florigene started with a white carnation and introduced a gene for delphinidin synthesis that they had obtained from a petunia. This resulted in lilac- and mauve-coloured carnations that have been given names such as 'Moondust' and 'Moonglow'. These new varieties now dominate the North and South American cut-flower markets but are not found in Europe because of opposition to genetically manipulated plants.

Following on from their success with carnations, Florigene scientists introduced the delphinidin gene into a variety of red rose known as 'Cardinal'. The addition of the blue delphinidin to the existing red pigment resulted in roses with deep burgundy flowers. Next the scientists knocked out the ability of the roses to make the red pigment and this generated a variety whose flowers have high levels of delphinidin. These flowers are not blue but an attractive shade of mauve similar in colour to those seen with varieties such as 'Blue Moon' and 'Vol de Nuit'. The difference is that whereas the latter varieties do not and cannot make a blue pigment, the genetically-engineered variety does. So, why does the genetically engineered variety have mauve flowers rather than blue ones? The reason has to do with the effect of acid on the colour of delphinidin. Like litmus paper, delphinidin is red in acid solutions and blue in alkaline solutions. Unfortunately, the cells that make up rose petals have a low pH value (pH 4.5) so the Florigene scientists now are looking for ways of reducing their acidity.

In 1840, the horticultural societies of Britain and Belgium offered a prize of 500,000 francs for the first person to produce a blue rose. Over 175 years later we are close but have not yet completed the task. Another competition, albeit a fictional one, was the quest for the black tulip made famous by Alexandre Dumas in his 1850 historical romance *The Black Tulip*. The story is set in Holland in 1672 at the height of tulipmania when the city of Haarlem offers a prize of 100,000 florins for the first person to produce a truly black tulip. This begins a competition between the country's best gardeners to win the money, the honour and the fame. Needless to say, the hero achieves the impossible only to be cheated and thrown in prison. Since he is rescued by his gaoler's beautiful daughter it is clear that this a love story rather than one about gardening. A second story by Polish poet Zbigniew Herbert tells of a poor Dutch shoemaker who comes across a black tulip by chance. He sells the bulb to the Union of Florists in Haarlem only to see them destroy it because they have one of their own. It is too much for him and he promptly dies.

Despite what Alexandre Dumas and Zbigniew Herbert wrote, a

naturally-occurring truly black tulip is impossible. For a flower to look black the pigments in the petals would have to completely absorb red, green yellow and blue light. That is, no light falling on the petals would be reflected and this never happens with the anthocyanins. There are many plants that people think of as being black, for example, *Ophiopogon nigrescens*, *Nemophila menziesii* 'Penny Black' and *Scabiosa atropurperea* 'Ace of Spades'. However, on closer examination it is clear that they are not black but deep purple. The same is true of the tulip known as 'Queen of Night': it may be sold as a black tulip but it is not. The only true black pigment that exists in Nature is melanin, the pigment found in black hair and dark skin. It is a totally different chemical to the anthocyanins and is not found in the plant world except in maple leaves infected with fungal 'tar spot'. No doubt the genetic engineers will try and introduce it into roses and tulips but it would serve them right if the flowers prematurely turned grey!

Favourite Fruit And Vegetables

A Dangerous Family

The family Solanacaeae, or potato family, is an interesting one for it contains some of the most poisonous plants known to man but also is the source of a number of very popular vegetables. Some members of the family such as the tomato and aubergine have both edible (fruit) and toxic parts (leaves). The name of the family may derive from the Latin verb '*solari*', meaning to soothe. If true then this would be a reference to the pharmacological properties of some of the better known psychoactive species. An alternative origin of the name is that it is derived from the perceived resemblance of some of the flowers to the sun and its rays. In support of this idea is the plant *Solanum nigrum* whose common name is the sunberry.

The vegetables that are produced by members of the Solanaceae are potatoes, tomatoes, bell and chilli peppers, tomatillos and aubergines but only the latter will be described here. The aubergine is the fruit of *Solanum melongena* and it has been cultivated in south-east Asia since 200BCE. The numerous Arabic and North African names for it, and the lack of Greek and Roman names suggest that it was introduced to Mediterranean Europe by Arabs. This probably occurred in the early Middle Ages. However, the aubergines of that time were not the plump purple fruits that we recognize today. According to 16th century herbalist John Gerard they were white, or occasionally yellow or brown, and about the size of a swan's egg. This could be the origin of 'eggplant' as the alternative name for the aubergine. However, in Italy the aubergine is known as *melanzana* which is a derivation of the Latin *mala insana* or mad apple. The word aubergine itself is derived from the Sanskrit '*vatinganah*' which means 'go away wind' or anti-flatulence vegetable.

The aubergine is used in cuisine in almost every country in the world and includes such well known dishes as moussaka (Greece), ratatouille (France) and Italian Melanzane alla Parmigiana (baked aubergines with Parmesan). They also are key ingredients in *Imam Bayildi*, a dish popular throughout the Arab world. According to legend the dish's name, which translates as the 'imam fainted', arose when one imam's wife made such a delicious version of this dish that her husband fainted with pleasure. If purchasing aubergines for cooking then remember the old maxim that aubergines and women past their best are very similar: they have slack skin and puckered posteriors!

The danger associated with the family Solanaceae is that almost all the 2,400 species in it produce a class of poisonous chemicals known as alkaloids. The three commonest alkaloids in the Solanaceae are hyoscyamine, atropine and scopolamine. They are produced by plants such as *Atropa* (deadly nightshade), *Brugmansia* (angel's trumpet), *Datura* (jimsonweed), *Hyoscyamus* (henbane), *Mandragora* (mandrake) and *Scopolia*. Another member of the Solanaceae is *Nicotiana* (tobacco) and it produces a different but equally well-known alkaloid: nicotine.

The medicinal use of the tropane alkaloids (atropine and scopolamine) was first described during the time of the Roman Empire by the Greek physician Dioscoroides. Mandrake root was bruised and the active ingredient (scopolamine) extracted with wine. This concoction was administered to patients to anaesthetize them for surgery. The Romans also knew that anaesthetic power of solanaceous plants was increased when combined with extracts from the opium poppy. This combination lives on today as a pre-operative medication and the presence of poppy heads and mandrake roots on the coat of arms of the Association of Anaesthetists of Great Britain and Ireland reminds us of the specialty's links with its past.

The Romans made great use of mandrake wine, applied on a sponge placed under the nose, as an adjunct to punishment by crucifixion. Mandrake wine was known to them as morion, or death wine, because of its ability to make victims appear dead when actually still alive. Indeed, so effective was it that centurions had orders to spear the bodies of victims before releasing them. Although the mandrake grows widely around the Mediterranean Sea it is not a native of northern Europe. However, henbane grows readily where mandrake does not and it can be used in a similar way although the hyoscyamine that it contains is not as potent as scopolamine.

The properties of henbane and its relatives were well known to Shakespeare for his plays contain many references to herbal medicines with sedative powers. For example, in one, Iago taunts Othello about the unfaithfulness of his wife Desdemona with

'Not poppy, nor mandragora,
Nor all the drowsy syrups of the world,
Shall ever medicine thee to that sweet sleep
Which thou owd'st yesterday.'

In *Romeo and Juliet*, Juliet asks Friar Lawrence how she might avoid marriage to Paris and he replies:

'Take thou this vial, being then in bed,
and this distilled liquor drink thou off:
When, presently, through all thy veins run
A cold and drowsy humour; for no pulse
Shall keep his native progress, but surcease:
No warmth, no breath, shall testify thou liv'st;
The roses in thy lips and cheeks shall fade
To paly ashes; thy eyes' windows fall,
Like death, when he shuts up the day of life;
Each part, depriv'd of supple government,
Shall, stiff and stark and cold, appear like death:
And in this borrow'd likeness of shrunk death
Thou shalt continue two-and-forty hours,
And then awake as from a pleasant sleep.'

Apart from the sudden awakening after a precise time, the description of the effects of the potion is uncannily like those of the mandrake wine used by the Romans. Shakespeare also was aware of the effects of excessive doses of these sedatives: Hamlet's father was murdered when a distillation of henbane was poured in his ear. In 1910, the infamous Dr Crippen murdered his wife by giving her an overdose of hyoscyamine (henbane) but was arrested in New York in what was the first use of the telegraph in a criminal case.

Hyoscyamine also has a close relative known as atropine or belladonna. Atropine gets its name from one of the three mythological Greek Fates, Atropos, who cut the thread of life! This is an appropriate name given that atropine was used to poison the troops of Marcus Antonius during the Parthian wars and it was used by the soldiers of Macbeth to poison an army of invading Danes. When applied to the eye, atropine causes enlargement of the pupils and Italian ladies used to do this in order to appear more beautiful hence the name 'bella donna' (beautiful lady). Both scopolamine and atropine are used by opthalmologists in a similar way today to facilitate examination of the eye. Scopolamine also finds use in medicines to prevent motion sickness although sufferers might prefer the more sedative effect experienced by Juliet.

Potatoes And Population Growth

Today, the potato is the most important single vegetable in the world as a whole. It achieved this status in a relatively short period of time and yet, amazingly, its origins are unclear. Indigenous to Central and South America, potatoes were probably domesticated first in Chile. They were discovered by Europeans at the time when the Spanish conquistador Francisco Pizarro was destroying the Incan empire. Some say that the Spanish brought them to Europe around 1570 and from there they made their way to England and Ireland. Others believe that Sir Walter Raleigh introduced them directly to England about 1586.

However the potato got to Europe, it did not prove popular with consumers of the time. It was recognized that this new plant could produce more food on less land than any other crop, particularly in northern Europe, but the populace largely rejected it. The reasons were manifold. Some people thought that they would cause leprosy on account of the lumpy, pock-marked appearance of the tuber. Protestants associated them with Catholicism because of their South American origins. Russian peasants thought them unclean and un-Christian and devout Scottish Presbyterians would not eat them because they were not mentioned in the Bible. Ireland was the exception. Much of the country is unsuited to the cultivation of cereals but ideal for potatoes. The impoverished Irish discovered that a few acres of marginal land could produce enough potatoes to feed a large family and its livestock. Furthermore, a diet of potatoes supplemented with cow's milk was nutritionally complete.

Eventually the potato's undeniable advantages over grain would convert all of Northern Europe but, Ireland apart, its acceptance was a slow process. In Germany, Frederick the Great had to force peasants to plant them by threatening to cut off their ears and noses as did Catherine the Great in Russia. In France, potatoes finally were established during the famine following the Seven Years War (1756–1763). Frenchman Antoine Parmentier had been fed potatoes in a prisoner-of-war camp in Germany. On his return to France he found his countrymen starving and set up potato soup kitchens throughout Paris. Today his name is honoured by the 'potage Parmentier' and 'potatoes Parmentier' seen on menus. King Louis XVI also played his part. He ordered that a field of potatoes be planted in the royal grounds and posted an elite guard to protect the crop – but only during the day. Convinced of the crop's value, the local peasants came every night and stole all the royal tubers.

In mainland Britain there still was resistance to the potato when it had been accepted elsewhere. However, a number of failures of the wheat harvest led to a debate about the introduction of the potato as a second staple crop. According to Arthur Young, a respected agronomist, potatoes would feed the poor when bread was dear and keep wages from rising. Radical journalist William Cobbett took a different view. Potatoes fed the Irish but impoverished them for, in less than a century, the Irish population had grown from 3 million to 8 million and wages had declined. The political economist Thomas Malthus argued that people are driven only by the desires for food and sex and it is the threat of starvation that keeps the population from exploding. According to Malthus, the potato removed the economic constraints that keep the population in check beyond the regular demand for labour. Potatoes were fuelling undesirable population growth.

Malthus was right in one sense. An Irish peasant only had the right to cultivate a small piece of land. As his family grew up and had children of their own, this plot had to feed more and more people. Initially, different varieties of potato had been grown but eventually the Lumper variety came to predominance. Although it did not have a very appealing taste, it was a heavy cropper even on poor soil and did not require much manure. It also was sensitive to *Phytophthora infestans*, the potato blight fungus. In 1843 and 1844 potato blight struck the US potato crop and Canada also suffered in 1844. It is thought that the disease travelled from there on trade ships and reached Ireland in 1845. That year was warm and wet, conditions favouring fungal growth, and half the potato crop was destroyed. The following spring people planted even more potatoes thinking that the blight was a one-off event. It was not and almost the entire crop of 1846 was wiped out. In 1847 the harvest improved but there was a relapse again in 1848 and 1849 coupled with an outbreak of cholera. What with death and mass migration, the population of Ireland never recovered.

What made the Irish vulnerable to famine was their reliance not only on one crop but one variety of one crop. Today, we know that genetic variation helps protect against the decimation of an entire crop by pests, disease, or climatic conditions. At the beginning of the 19th century a survey recorded at least a dozen varieties of potato in one Irish county alone. However, the rapid rise of the Lumper variety eliminated this genetic variation. Although the famine had many more causes than those described above, the disaster would not have been nearly so bad if more genetically variable potatoes had been planted. Some potatoes would have carried the right genes to make it through the epidemic and more of the resistant varieties could have been planted in the years following the first epidemic.

Returning to the Andes, the home of the potato, monoculture is not a problem. The reason for this is the terrain. Potatoes are grown on steep hillsides and the microclimate changes with every change in altitude or orientation of the valley. A potato variety that thrives on one side of a ridge at one altitude may well languish on a plot on the other side. So the Incas developed a manner of farming that is the exact opposite of monoculture: a different variety for each ecological niche. These cultivated varieties probably interbreed with one another generating yet more varieties. In this way the Peruvians have avoided catastrophic losses from pests and diseases.

Despite the lessons of the Irish potato famine, many countries still depend on genetically uniform crops. In the US in 1970, over one billion dollars worth of corn was lost to a fungal infection. Again, in the 1980s, dependence on a single type of grapevine root resulted in an attack of a new race of grape phylloxera and two million acres had to be replanted with new vines. Even more astonishing is the dependence of American farmers on a single variety of potato, even though this is driven by the desire of fast food chains to have French Fries that taste the same everywhere. So, to keep their crops free from disease they spray them with pesticides to prevent aphid transmission of viruses and with fungicides. The use of a variety of potato genetically-engineered to be resistant to insects may reduce the use of pesticides but creates yet another monoculture. Will we never learn?

The World's Favourite Vegetable

Four hundred years ago the potato was barely known outside of a few countries in South America whereas today it is the most widely eaten vegetable. In those 400 years the potato has been processed in every way imaginable: boiled, roasted, fried, chipped, crisped, mashed as well as being pureed into soup, but where did these innovations come from? Dehydrated potatoes, those stalwarts of expedition cooks and busy housewives, are thought of as a modern invention so it might come as a surprise to know that they have been around for thousands of years. The Indians of the high country of Peru developed the original method of dehydrating potatoes: they simply spread them out in the sun and let them dry out. At high elevations, especially late in the season, the potatoes will freeze and this helps them to dry faster. The product obtained by this method might not satisfy Western palates but certainly meets the needs of the Indians. Given that remains of stores of these dried potatoes have been uncovered in prehistoric ruins, freeze-dried potatoes are nothing new.

For much of the 19th century, 'baked potato men' plied the streets of major cities selling hot potatoes in their jackets to passers-by. At the height of their trade there were over 250 such potato sellers in London alone. Of course, no self-respecting English gentleman or gentlewoman would do anything as vulgar as eat on the street. However, on cold winter days they often bought the baked potatoes as hand warmers.

One of the most popular ways of eating potatoes is in the form of chips (UK and Commonwealth) or frites (France) or French fries (North America). In English-speaking countries outside of North America the term 'French fries' is used only by fast-food restaurants serving narrow-cut (shoestring) fries. Traditional 'chips' usually are cut much thicker and cooked twice to make them crisp on the outside and fluffy on the inside. The Belgians are noted for claiming that French fries are Belgian in origin and cite documentation from 1680. Many attribute the invention of French fries to the French but in France they are often thought of as Belgian. If this is true then the Belgians at last are famous for something other than TinTin and Hercule Poirot! Prior to becoming President in 1801, Thomas Jefferson travelled extensively in Europe and it is believed that he introduced French fries to North America. Certainly, recipes for French fries do not turn up in American cookbooks until after his presidency.

The popularity of French fries has been heavily influenced by fast-food chains. Up until the early 1950s, potatoes were hand peeled and cut into batons in individual restaurants. Then, in the early 1950s, Jack Simplot of the J.R. Simplot Company invented the frozen French fry. He signed a deal with Ray Kroc of McDonald's and the resulting reduction in preparation time fuelled the rapid expansion of the franchise. The present variation in frozen French fries is the so-called 'oven chip' but this is a poor imitation of the chips that I remember from my childhood. They were cooked in beef fat, had a high content of dangerous saturated fats, and were delicious – a word I could not use with today's specimens.

The potato crisp, or potato chip in North America, is believed to have been invented in 1853 by George Crum. He was a chef at Moon's Lake House near Saratoga Springs, New York. He was fed up with one customer, reputedly wealthy rail magnate Cornelius Vanderbilt, who kept sending his fried potatoes back because they were too thick and soggy. Incensed, he sliced the potatoes very thinly and fried them to a crisp so that they could not be pierced by a fork. Then he overdid the seasoning. To his amazement, the diner was delighted and ate the lot. From then on they became a regular menu item.

Eventually potato crisps spread beyond restaurants and started to be mass produced for home consumption. Initially they were stored in tins but it was not uncommon for the crisps to become stale or damp. Then Laura Scudder invented the crisp bag by ironing together two pieces of wax paper. This created an airtight seal and kept the crisps fresh until the bag was opened. Today, crisps are packaged in plastic bags and nitrogen gas is blown into the bags before sealing: this lengthens shelf life and provides protection from crushing.

Potato crisps were not available in Britain until 1920 with the formation of Smiths Potato Crisps. Older readers will recall that these were sold with a little blue bag of salt and often were chewed inadvertently in the darkness of a cinema. It is rumoured that during the Second World War the blue bags were not the only things found in Smith's crisps. Sometimes the women packing the crisps would include little pieces of paper with their names and addresses on them to draw the attention of any lonely soldiers. Golden Wonder crisps, started in Arbroath in 1947 by Scottish baker William Alexander and named after the local potato variety, were the first to produce ready-salted crisps. They also were the first to introduce flavoured crisps – the infamous cheese and onion variety.

The potato crisp continues to evolve. Pringles are made by extruding or pressing dough made from ground potatoes into the familiar potato crisp shape before frying. This makes crisps that are very uniform in size and shape and can be stacked and packaged in rigid tubes. Another innovation is blue crisps which hit the UK market in 2003. They are made from potatoes with blue flesh and many people are surprised that such potatoes exist. However, in South America there are many coloured potatoes including ones with purple, pink, orange or yellow flesh. Coloured potatoes have been introduced to the UK market as novelty items but they will survive only if they have some desirable quality. One such potato may be the variety Mayan Gold launched in 2006 by the Scottish Crop Research Institute. It has yellow flesh and scores well in taste panels but also cooks in just five minutes.

Potatoes still are making history. In 1995 the potato became the first vegetable to be grown in space. The National Aeronautics and Space

Administration (NASA) worked with plant breeders to develop super-nutritious varieties to feed astronauts on long space voyages. Let us hope that they do not get infected with potato blight or the astronauts will have had their chips!

Taxing Tomatoes And Other Tales

The tomato probably is the second most popular vegetable after the potato. It is cultivated and consumed throughout the Western world and used as a mainstay of salads. Generations of children have been reared on tomato soup and would not consider a main course to be complete without lashings of tomato sauce. However, like the potato, the tomato is a relative newcomer to our diet.

According to geneticists, the way to identify the origin of a crop plant is to look for the geographical region which has the greatest diversity of that crop. On this basis, tomatoes probably originated along the Western coast of South America. At least eight species of wild tomato are found today in the region stretching from northern Chile through Peru to Ecuador. From Peru the tomato seems to have made its way northwards into Central America and Mexico. The Spanish explorer Cortez conquered the area that now encompasses Mexico City and brought tomatoes back to Europe. However, these were cultivated tomatoes of the type we know today as cherry tomatoes. Although the fruits were small by modern standards, they still were much larger than the fruits found on wild tomatoes. Clearly, the tomato had been domesticated but where and by whom?

The ancient Peruvians decorated their pottery with pictures of crops but no artifacts have been found that depict tomatoes. Nor does the tomato feature in any early Peruvian written material. On the other hand, the tomato does feature in Aztec writings including recipes for a concoction of peppers, salt and tomatoes. Today we would consider it a recipe for salsa! The absence of anything resembling the cultivated tomato in Peru and neighbouring countries also suggests that domestication occurred in Central America.

The tomatoes that Cortez brought back to Spain about 1521 were called *pome dei Moro* meaning Moor's apple. In Italy they were called *pomo d'oro* (golden apple) suggesting that the first tomatoes to reach the Old World had yellow skins. In France they were called *pomme d'amour* (love apple) but it is not clear if they got that name because they were considered an aphrodisiac or because a Frenchman misunderstood a Spanish lady whispering *pome dei Moro* in his ear. Unlike their continental counterparts, the British initially did not eat tomatoes but used them to remove pustules on the skin! It was the mid-18th century before they recognized their culinary properties.

The tomato was taken to North America by the colonists but at first was grown as an ornamental plant. Due to the French influence in New Orleans the tomato was used early on in creole cooking but acceptance elsewhere was patchy. George Washington Carver, the man responsible for the introduction of peanut butter, exhorted his poor Alabaman neighbours to eat tomatoes to improve their diet but had little success. The real problem was that tomatoes were seen as relatives of the deadly nightshade and were thought to be toxic. Doubts about the safety of the tomato supposedly were put to rest by Colonel Robert Gibbon Johnson in 1820. He announced that at noon on 26 September he would consume a bushel of tomatoes on the steps of the Boston courthouse. Crowds turned out to see him die whilst a local band played funereal music and were sorely disappointed when he did not. The story almost certainly is apocryphal but it makes an entertaining read.

Tomatoes now are eaten regularly by almost everyone and it is hard to believe that they once were considered dangerous. In fact, today tomatoes are considered to be extremely good for you on account of their carotenoid content. Carotenoids are the pigments that give tomatoes their red colour and the principal carotenoid in tomatoes is lycopene. Not only does this get converted to vitamin A in the human body but it is now believed to be a very potent anti-oxidant which can destroy cancer-causing chemicals. Because studies have shown that eating lots of tomatoes on a regular basis results in a reduced risk of cancer, breeders are developing new varieties with enhanced lycopene content. More recently it has been discovered that tomatoes also contain a compound that can reduce blood clotting and that drinking a large glass of tomato juice every day can reduce the risk of a heart attack.

Benefits aside, it is hard to conceive of modern cooking in the absence of tomatoes. Without tomatoes there would be far fewer pasta dishes and no minestrone soup or cacciatore or osso buco. Most of all, there would be no traditional pizza, that great dish invented by a restauranteur in Naples in the late 1880s. Supposedly it was invented to celebrate the visit of Queen Margarite, the first Italian monarch since Napoleon's conquest of Italy. The restaurant made the pizza from ingredients that represented the colours of the new Italian flag: red, white and green. The basil topping was green, the mozzarella cheese was white and, obviously, the tomato sauce was red. Thus Pizza Margarite was created.

Like the story of Colonel Johnson, the story about Pizza Margarite may well be apocryphal but the story of John Nix and his battle with the US Supreme Court is not. In 1883 the US Congress passed a Tariff Act that imposed a tax of 10 per cent on all imported vegetables. John Nix was a tomato importer and he believed that tomatoes should be exempt from the tax because they have seeds and therefore botanically are fruit. The case eventually reached the Supreme Court in 1893. In his judgement, Mr Justice Gray ruled that tomatoes are vegetables for tax purposes because tomatoes are eaten with main meals and not desserts. To this day tomatoes are still classified in the United States as vegetables. Whilst the decision of Mr Justice Gray might seem like common sense, it more likely was made to protect US tomato growers and to generate tax revenues. After all, why should the truth interfere with what is politic?

Tomahtoes And Tomaytoes

Tomatoes were first domesticated in Central America long before Cortez discovered them and brought them to Europe early in the 16th century. These tomatoes were yellow-skinned and most probably of the type that are known today as cherry tomatoes. Catholic priests were responsible for the introduction much later of red-skinned varieties. Although the origin of the red-skinned varieties is unclear it is likely that they too came from Central America. Whilst the popularity of tomatoes in the Old World increased in the 300 years following their introduction, there was little change in the varieties grown. That all changed in the 19th century with the development of tomato breeding programmes, first in Europe and then later in the United States. Today, there are tomatoes that have been grown for growth type, size, shape, solids content, colour, disease resistance and ripening behaviour although in many cases taste has been a casualty.

Tomato breeders classify tomato varieties as determinate or indeterminate. Determinate types, also known as bush types, bear a full crop of tomatoes all at once and top off at a specific height. These are good choices for growing in containers. Indeterminate cultivars are the types favoured by commercial growers. They develop into vines that never top off and continue producing until killed by frost but need to be staked or caged to stop them sprawling over the ground. Some heirloom varieties are classified as 'vigorous determinate' or 'semi-determinate'. These top off like determinate varieties but produce more than one crop of tomatoes in a season.

Tomatoes come in various fruit types and the commonest ones are plum, beefsteak, salad and cherry. Plum tomatoes are oval shaped and their firm flesh means that they keep their shape when bottled or canned. Beefsteak tomatoes are the largest varieties. Their pulp cavity is relatively small and always compressed and distorted by the extensive placenta wall. This gives it a marbled appearance that resembles raw steak hence their name. Because of the limited pulp cavity, beefsteak tomatoes hold together on slicing and this makes them the choice for sandwiches in the catering trade. Salad tomatoes are the type traditionally grown in the UK. Their abundant pulp tends to fall out if the fruit is sliced and they do not reduce well for sauces but their size means that they can be halved or quartered for inclusion in salads. Cherry tomatoes are really smaller versions of salad tomatoes that have been bred as a snacking food.

Commercial tomato cultivars have been bred for their size, shape, disease and pest resistance, and suitability for mechanized picking. More recently, the purchasing power of supermarkets has added other necessary traits: uniformity of size and shape and travelling and keeping qualities. Whereas taste is low down on the list of priorities for commercial tomatoes it is the major factor in the selection of varieties by the amateur gardener. The best flavours often reside in so-called heirloom varieties; that is, old varieties that have been maintained because of appealing attributes.

Many of the heirloom tomatoes have colourful histories, particularly the US varieties. A good example is the cultivar Mortgage Lifter raised by a West Virginian named Charlie. He owned a car repair shop that fell on hard times during the Depression as people could not afford to run their cars. A keen tomato grower, he had crossed a number of varieties and eventually generated a plant that produced fruits weighing two pounds each. He sold the plants for a dollar each, claiming that they could feed a family of six, and in a few years had cleared his mortgage. A French variety called Carolina is considered a rare delicacy among tomato connoisseurs and is the only cultivar traditionally served with Ortolan, a dish made from fig-fed songbirds.

Tomatoes are often picked when still green and then artificially ripened with ethylene gas. Tomatoes ripened this way tend to keep longer but have poorer colour. In 1994, a Californian company called Calgene developed a genetically-engineered tomato that had a long shelf life. However, consumers were very wary of genetically-engineered foodstuffs and the product was withdrawn in 1997. Slow-ripening varieties have been developed by 'conventional' genetic means by crossing a non-ripening variety with ordinary cultivars. They are known as 'Thrushworthy Bumbletots' as this is the name of the machine used to clean tomatoes before processing.

The two most popular ways of processing tomatoes are for soup and ketchup. Soup has its origins in medieval times when peasants lived on thin gruel from a stockpot that was topped up endlessly. This gruel was served over thick pieces of bread known as 'soppes' and eaten without a spoon. Eventually the gruel itself became known as soup. In the US in 1869, the Joseph A. Campbell Preservative Company was established to produce canned tomatoes and soups. In 1897 they had a major breakthrough when scientist John Dorrance conceived of removing much of the water from soup before canning it. Thus condensed soup was invented and it enabled the equivalent of a 30 ounce can of soup to be packaged in 10 ounces and sold for one third the price. The product was so successful that the company was renamed the Campbell Soup Company.

Ketchup was developed hundreds of years ago by the Chinese and Malays. They used the brine from pickled fish as a dipping sauce and called it '*kachiap*'. Traders brought the concept to Britain where the product was modified by the addition of walnuts and mushrooms and the name evolved to '*catsup*'. Colonial Americans further enhanced the product by the addition of tomatoes and sugar. Initially the product was very watery but gradually the product was thickened as tomatoes with high solids contents were bred. Initially called '*catchup*', the name evolved into the present day ketchup.

So, what will be the next changes to tomatoes? In 1984 over twelve million tomato seeds were blasted into space where they stayed for six years. After being retrieved by the crew of Columbia they were distributed to more than three million schoolchildren in 35 countries. No rampaging killer tomatoes were created – much to the disappointment of fans of the cult spoof movie 'Attack of the Killer Tomatoes'. Older readers will remember the 1963 Alfred Hitchcock movie *The Birds* in which birds begin attacking humans. Fiction became fact when this actually happened in 1975. Even with genetic engineering it is hard to conceive of tomatoes revolting against humanity.

Columbus, Capsicums And Chillies

The *Capsicum* genus is a diverse plant group within the potato family (*Solanaceae*) whose fruits range from the sweet, mild bell peppers (often called capsicums) to the fiery hot chilli peppers. Members of the genus have been part of the human diet in the Americas since 7500 BCE and were cultivated by prehistoric peoples from Peru and Bolivia in South America through Mexico to Colorado and New Mexico in the United States. Christopher Columbus encountered them when he discovered the Americas in 1492 and called them red peppers because of the similarity in taste to the black pepper although the latter is a totally different plant. The peppers that Columbus brought back to Europe quickly gained notoriety for being much more pungent than the black pepper then sourced from the Caucasus. These new peppers were easy to grow and this had two consequences. First, pepper no longer was a luxury spice that only the wealthy could afford. Second, its cultivation spread across India, Asia and Africa and it was incorporated into local cuisines. Today, spicy hot dishes are commonplace in most parts of the world.

Capsicum terminology is extremely confusing for the fruits of the most widely grown species, *C. annuum*, vary enormously in terms of pungency, colour, shape, flavour, size and use. At one end of the spectrum are the bell peppers, discovered in Panama in 1699 by an English pirate called Wafer. The term 'bell' refers to the fruit's blocky shape and its characteristic four lobes. Bell peppers are non-pungent, can be eaten raw and one pepper contains ten times the recommended daily vitamin C intake. Traditionally, bell peppers were green in colour. However, if the peppers are left on the bush for longer they turn from green to red and then yellow and in the process they become sweeter. Pimentos are another non-pungent variety of red pepper. Other varieties of *C.annuum* are more pungent and they include paprika (mild), jalapenos, poblano and chiltepin. Two other cultivated species are *C. frutescens*, which includes the cayenne and tabasco peppers, and *C. chinense* which includes the hottest peppers (naga, habanero and Scotch bonnet).

The substances that give chilli peppers their pungency or 'heat' are a family of chemicals related to capsaicin. The stem end of each pod has glands that produce the capsaicins and these chemicals flow down through the pod under the influence of gravity. Thus, the hottest part of the chilli pepper is the top of the pod. Pungency is expressed in Scoville heat units (SHU) and is an organoleptic test that uses a panel of five human tasters. This panel tastes samples of chilli and records the dilution of the sample at which no heat can be detected. The hotter the sample, the greater the dilution required to eliminate pungency. Using this assessment method, bell peppers have a score of 0, jalapenos 3,000–6,000 SHU and habaneros 300,000 SHU. BBC Gardeners' World in 2006 found that the *C. chinense* variety Dorset Naga had a score of over 1 million SHU. The Scoville test has its limitations. Tasters have to be trained and their ability to test many samples is restricted by taste fatigue and the heat of the test solution. Being a taster certainly brings new meaning to the phrase 'hot work'!

Although food containing chilli peppers tastes hot, the capsaicin from the peppers stimulates a region of the brain that lowers body temperature. In fact, many people in subtropical and tropical climates regularly consume moderately hot peppers because they help them tolerate the heat. So, how do we explain the liking of people from temperate climates for fiercely pungent curries and the like? One possibility is that they are seeking a 'capsaicin high', a euphoric sensation resulting from the release of endorphins by the brain following the ingestion of large amounts of capsaicin. Another explanation is that eating chillies is a 'constrained risk' analogous to riding a roller coaster: the pain and fear can be enjoyed because they are not physically harmful.

When people eat food with a high chilli content that is too hot for them to bear, they often will try to cool their mouth down by drinking water. This is a mistake. Capsaicin is insoluble in water and drinking water will only spread it around the mouth. A much better idea is to eat or drink something that is fatty such as butter, yoghurt or milk. Capsaicin is able to dissolve freely in the fat and this will remove it from the surface of the mouth. Drinking alcohol also will help.

Food containing chilli peppers can taste very hot even when it is not thermally hot. Why should this be? The burning sensation associated with chillies results from the binding of capsaicin to receptors on the tongue and the surface of the mouth. These receptors, and identical ones found all over the skin, normally react to heat and physical abrasion. Regardless of how these receptors are stimulated, be it from a friction 'burn' or through eating chillies, the brain reacts as if the tissue concerned has been burned. If excessive capsaicin is applied to the skin, or if it is applied over a prolonged period, there is depletion of a chemical (substance P) in nerve endings that transmits pain sensations. This explains why you may have no feeling in your mouth for some time after eating a very hot curry. It also explains why capsaicin is being used topically to treat the pain associated with shingles, cluster headaches and psoriasis. However, the therapeutic use of chilli is nothing new: the Aztecs used it to treat toothache.

There have been some innovative suggestions for alternative uses of capsaicin. It has been tried as a barnacle repellant, to repel rats and mice from gnawing power cables, to keep squirrels from eating bird seed (birds cannot sense capsaicin), to stop elephants rampaging through villages, and as a deterrent for drugs of abuse. In the United States, anti-riot and anti-mugger sprays containing capsaicin now have replaced mace and tear gas. If the spray comes in contact with skin, especially eyes or mucous membranes, it is very painful and immediately incapacitates the recipient.

Certain varieties of chillies are grown for their decorative qualities rather than for consumption. The interest in them as ornamental plants comes from their dense foliage and their unusual pod shapes. The pods come in a range of colours and it is not unusual to see four or five different colours on a single plant at any one time. These ornamental chillies sometimes are known as Christmas peppers because the fruits are produced around the festive season. In the southwestern United States, particularly New Mexico, mature red chillies are threaded on strings known as ristras and hung over the entrance of a house as a symbol of hospitality – and a warning to your tastebuds?

Know Your Onions

Onions may have been one of the earliest cultivated crops because they were less perishable than other foods of the time and could be kept for later consumption when food might be scarce. The fact that they are easy to grow and can be cultivated in a variety of soils and climates would have enhanced their attractiveness when man moved from being a hunter-gatherer to a farmer. Although the place and time of the onion's origin are unknown, onions almost certainly featured in the pre-historic diet.

The earliest records of onion cultivation come from China and India and are about 5,000 years old. In Egypt, onions can be traced back to 3500 BCE and in Sumer (present day Iraq) to 2500 BCE. One Sumerian text tells of someone ploughing over the onion patch of a city governor: one wonders what became of the guilty party! According to the book of Numbers in the Bible, the onion (*Allium cepa*) and its close relatives garlic (*Allium sativum*) and leeks (*Allium porrium*) were eaten by the Israelites in Egypt prior to the Exodus.

Onions were an object of worship in ancient Egypt. Because of the circle-within-a-circle structure of the bulbs, Egyptians equated onions with eternal life. Many mummies have been found with onions placed adjacent to various parts of the body. In the case of King Ramses IV, who died in 1160 BCE, the onions were in his eye sockets. Some Egyptologists have theorized that the onions were used because it was thought that their strong scent would prompt the dead to breathe again. Others believe their use relates to their strong antiseptic properties. Both onions and garlic featured in the diet of the workers involved in the construction of the Great Pyramids (~3200 BCE). Given the importance of onions to Egyptians and the low status of the workers this might have been to prevent spread of infectious diseases in the very crowded workers' quarters.

Onions, garlic and leeks feature in the first 'cookbook' that now is kept at Yale University. This is a pair of Babylonian clay tablets dated to 1750 BCE that detail about 35 recipes. Since few people of this period could read the recipes clearly were intended for those in charge of major households. Many references to onions also can be found in *Apicius*, a collection of Roman cookery recipes from the fourth or fifth century CE.

One of the earliest medical treatises is the Indian Charaka Samhita that was written some time between 400 and 200 BCE. It claims that onions are a diuretic and good for the digestion, heart, eyes and blood. In the first century CE, the Greek physician Dioscorides noted several medicinal uses of onions. Onions also were used to fortify athletes for the Olympic Games: large amounts were eaten and competitors rubbed onions on their bodies. In the first century CE, Pliny the Elder wrote of the medicinal qualities of onions and believed them beneficial for a long list of complaints. He also described the cultivation of onions in Pompei before the eruption of Vesuvius that killed him. During the excavation of the ruins at Pompei the location of onions could be determined from the telltale cavities left behind. A somewhat unusual use of onions is the treatment of gunshot wounds, a practice that started in the 16th century. During the American Civil War, General Grant refused to move his Union troops without a supply of onions.

Chemical analysis of onion bulbs has shown that they contain a number of compounds that **might** have a beneficial effect on human health. One such compound is allicin which is formed as soon as an onion is cut and has potent antifungal, anti-thrombotic and anti-inflammatory activity. Unfortunately, allicin is destroyed by cooking and decomposes rapidly on storage so that it will be absent from garlic preparations obtained from healthfood stores. Onion bulbs also are rich in flavonoids such as quercetin that are free radical scavengers and so might help in the fight against cancer. However, very few proper clinical trials have been done to determine if raw and cooked onions or garlic extracts really improve health.

Everyone knows that slicing onions can lead to tears and this is the consequence of the release of a chemical called propenesulphenic acid. In the presence of oxygen this chemical is transformed into the volatile lacrimatory factor thiopropanal-S-oxide. The lacrimatory factor dissolves in the fluid bathing the eyes and breaks down into a number of compounds including sulphuric acid, hence the burning sensation. The eye responds to this assault by producing copious tears to dilute and wash away the offending acid. Chilling onions before cutting them or cutting them under water can greatly reduce the formation of the lachrymatory factor. Attempts have been made to develop onions that do not make us cry and a New Zealand group finally has been successful. The effort required surprised one comedian who thought it should be easy since food scientists had little difficulty in giving us tasteless bread.

Another undesirable property of onions, particularly when raw, is that anyone that eats them is left with a foul-smelling breath. Garlic is even worse in this regard. As one anonymous poet put it:

If leekes you like but do their smell disleek,
Eate onions and you shalle not smelle the leeke.
If you of onions would the scent expelle,
Eat garlicke, that shall drowne the onyon's smelle

At least with onions the problem can be eliminated by cooking them as the author Jonathan Swift noted:

But lest your kissing should be spoil'd,
Your onions must be thorough boil'd.

Cooking is of little help with garlic. Furthermore, eat a lot of it and the noxious metallic sulphurous smell seeps out of the skin. However, this will keep vampires and mosquitoes at bay. In the same way, underplanting roses with alliums should keep blackfly away.

Leeks were the favourite vegetable of the Roman Emperor Nero who consumed it most often in soup form. Today, leeks are key ingredients in a number of traditional soups including vichyssoise, cock-a-leekie (chicken and leek), leek and potato and Scotch broth. However, in Britain, leeks are not associated with soup so much as with the Welsh. The leek, along with the daffodil, is a national emblem of Wales. According to legend, St David ordered his soldiers to wear them in their hats for identification purposes during a battle with pagans in a leek field. Quite how his soldiers would have complied with this order is difficult to comprehend. Nevertheless, Shakespeare makes reference to the wearing of leeks in *Henry V*. In this play, Henry tells Fluellen he is wearing a leek 'for I am Welsh, you know, good countryman'. Today, if you want to see a Welshman wearing a leek on any day other than St David's day (1 March) you will need to find a member of the Welsh Guards. Officers and men of the Welsh Guards have a representation of a leek as their cap badge and, when wearing ceremonial dress, as a collar badge.

An Apple For The Teacher

And when the woman saw that the tree was good for food, and that it was a delight to the eyes, and that the tree was to be desired to make one wise, she took of the fruit thereof, and did eat; and she gave also unto her husband with her, and he did eat…

We all know what it was that Adam and Eve did – or do we? In his wonderful paintings, the 16th century artist Cranach the Elder shows Eve presenting Adam with an apple. Many other artists did the same. But, nowhere in the book of Genesis does it say that it was an apple: it only refers to 'forbidden fruit'. Contemporary Biblical scholars now think that a pomegranate or a fig would have been more likely. Nevertheless, we can still enjoy the words of Thomas Hood (1799–1845):

When Eve upon the first of Men
The apple press'd with specious cant,
Oh! What a thousand pities then
That Adam was not Adamant!

Assuming that the Garden of Eden really existed, would apples have grown in it? The answer depends on the geographical location of the Garden and there have been many claims: Ethiopia, Java, Sri Lanka and Bristol, Florida and (by Mormons) Jackson County, Missouri. Most people, however, put the Garden near the confluence of the Tigris and Euphrates rivers in what today is Iraq. Given that apple trees need at least 900 hours below 7°C if they are to flower and set fruit it is unlikely that Eve could find an apple with which to tempt Adam. So, how did apples become associated with evil?

Sweetness is a taste sensation that many people quickly learn to crave. The best example of this is the behaviour of young children following their first exposure to chocolate. But, until the discovery of the West Indies by the early explorers, Western civilizations would have had little access to sugar other than in the form of honey. However, many apples are sweet and to those not exposed to sugar the way we are today they would have been a real treat. Is this the reason why Eve is supposed to have tempted Adam with an apple?

If apples did not come from the Garden of Eden then where did they originate? Geneticists believe that the origins of a plant are the place where there is the greatest genetic diversity. On this basis the apple originated near Alma-Ata ('father of the apples') in Kazakhstan. A tree known as *Malus sieversii* grows wild there as well as in the neighbouring countries of Kyrgyzstan and Tajikistan and in Xinjiang province of China. DNA analysis strongly suggests that a tree from this area was the progenitor of today's cultivated apple (*M. domestica*). The wild *M. sieversii* grows to 60 feet and produces a wide range of apple-like fruits. The tastiest of these would have been selected by travellers on the infamous Silk Route, which traverses Kazakhstan, and apple cultivation gradually would have spread westwards.

For the earliest people trying to domesticate the apple tree there was a key problem: most apples need to be fertilised by pollen from a different variety. This means that the seeds from an apple do not breed true. The only way to propagate a tree that produces tasty apples is to graft it to a suitable rootstock. The Chinese are credited with inventing tree grafting somewhere between 5000 and 2000 BCE. It is not known when this invaluable skill was transferred down the Silk Route but it was known to the Romans: Pliny the Elder in the first century described 37 varieties of cultivated apple.

Cultivated apples were introduced to Britain first by the Romans and again around the time of the Norman Conquest in 1066. They really became important when King Henry VIII instructed his fruiterer, Richard Harris, to establish large scale orchards in Kent and to scour the known world for the best varieties. By the mid-19th century over 600 varieties were known in Britain and, today, the National Apple Collection at Brogdale in Kent houses over 2,000 varieties. A similar collection in Tasmania has over 500 varieties.

The early colonists took apple trees to North America, Australia and New Zealand but grafted Old World trees fared badly in the New World. Not surprisingly, trees selected for good performance in the English weather and soil failed to satisfy when grown under different conditions. New varieties were required and here the variability of apple seeds was a real bonus. Apple seeds were sown in their new habitat and allowed to develop into trees or 'pippins'. Those trees that cropped well and produced apples with desirable properties then were propagated by grafting to generate varieties unique to their location. As a consequence, there are over 7,500 known varieties of apples in the World and most of these have been grown in only one country.

No story about the origin of apples would be complete without a mention of the man known as Johnny Appleseed. His real name was John Chapman and he was an American apple fanatic. In the early 19th century he travelled by makeshift boat from the Allegheny River in the East as far west as Ohio. With him he had bags of apple seed that he scattered as he travelled thereby initiating orchards of undomesticated trees. Although grafted apples were commonplace at the time Chapman would have nothing to do with them. 'They can improve apples that way,' he is supposed to have said, 'but that is only a device of man, and it is wicked to cut up trees that way. The correct method is to select good seeds and plant them in good ground and God only can improve the apple.'

Apple trees must have been a godsend to the early colonists. Varieties could be selected that produced eating apples or cooking apples or apples destined for juice or cider. If a real kick was wanted, the cider was allowed to partially freeze and the ice discarded to generate applejack with a high content of alcohol. Furthermore, once an apple tree was past its useful life, the wood could be used to form mallets or logs for fires and the woodchips used to smoke foods. The potential health benefits of eating apples were not realised until much later. The statement that 'an apple a day keeps the doctor away' was first made in 1904 and probably was an early marketing ploy.

Certain apple varieties have good keeping qualities and in mediaeval times they would have been a very important source of good food during the winter. Therefore a good harvest would have been very important and in certain parts of England this led to the custom of wassailing. Villagers would gather round the apple trees with shotguns or pots and pans and make a lot of noise to scare off demons. The biggest and best tree then was selected and cider poured over its roots whilst pieces of toast soaked in cider were hung in its branches. Finally, everyone would sing the wassail song that was nothing more than a prayer for a good harvest the next year.

We are all familiar with the expression 'An apple for the teacher' and assume that it is associated with teacher's pets and bribery. The truth is quite different. In the US, Denmark and Sweden, a polished apple is a traditional gift for a teacher. This stems from the 16–18th centuries when teachers were so poorly paid that parents would compensate the teacher by providing food. As apples were a very common crop, teachers often would be given baskets of them by students. These apples would have provided the teacher with a source of sweetness which probably explains their association with sycophancy – it is the Adam and Eve story all over again.

Who Was Granny Smith?

There are four basic properties of apples that determine which varieties that any individual prefers: sweetness, tartness (acidity), texture and, to a lesser extent, aroma. The amount of sugars and malic acid in each variety determines the balance of sweetness and tartness in the fruit. The more malic acid and the fewer sugars present, the stronger the flavour. The texture of an apple depends on the way the tissue ruptures when the flesh is broken on eating. This in turn is dependent on the chemistry of the cell walls of the fruit. In crunchy tissues, rupture occurs across the cell wall resulting in cell breakage and release of juice. In soft or mealy tissues the rupture occurs between cells and much less juice is released. The aroma of a particular variety is the result of a subtle blend of over 250 different volatile compounds within the apple.

The Brogdale Horticultural Trust in Kent maintains a collection of over 2,000 apple varieties. The oldest variety that the Trust has is Old English. First recorded in 1204, this was the main dessert apple in England well into the 18th century. The UK is the only country that grows apples especially for cooking and the first culinary variety was Costard. Costermongers originally were sellers of Costard apples but today the word means a person who sells all fruit and vegetables from a barrow in the street. Queen Charlotte, wife of George III, is credited with introducing the Queen's apple from Germany to Britain. This apple was cooked into a pudding that became known as Apple Charlotte.

Another very old apple variety is the Lady apple or Api, after the Etruscan who supposedly developed it about 2,000 years ago. It was first documented in 1628 during the French Renaissance and was considered by Louis IV to be the only apple worth growing. The Lady apple was grown throughout Europe and introduced to North America by the colonialists. It keeps well until at least March and so was considered a Christmas treat by the early American settlers. Lady apples are very small, about one and one half inches across, and are flattened at both ends and this makes them favourites for Christmas decorations.

The rarest apple variety that we know of is the Bardsey that comes from tiny Bardsey Island off the Llyn peninsula of North Wales. It was first discovered in September 2000 and came from a single gnarled and twisted tree growing hard against a house. This tree is believed to be the sole survivor of an orchard planted on the island and tended by monks over 1,000 years ago although the house was built about 1870. Both the fruit and the tree are unusual. The fruit is pink, juicy and lemon-scented and needs no sugar if cooked whilst the tree appears to be extremely disease resistant.

To apple connoisseurs the quintessential English apple is Cox's Orange Pippin. The term 'orange' in the context of apple varieties refers to an apple with an orange flush. The original tree of Cox's Orange Pippin was grown by Richard Cox, a retired brewer living at Lawn Cottage in Colnbrook, Buckinghamshire. This tree no longer exists having been blown down in a gale about 1911. According to an article in *The Gardener's Magazine* in 1902, Mr Cox sowed nine pips from an apple of the Ribston variety that had been pollinated by a variety known as Blenheim Orange. One of the resulting pippins (trees derived from pips) became Cox's Orange Pippin and another Cox's Pomona. The exact date of origin of Cox's Orange Pippin is not known but is believed to be about 1830. This date fits with other information: apple trees take 10 years to fruit and the variety was grown commercially according to The Gardener's Chronicle of 1857.

Cox's Orange Pippin remains unsurpassed for its richness and complexity of flavour, this complexity changing as the apple matures in the months after picking. Unfortunately it is a difficult variety to grow: it needs a warm dry climate and it is very prone to disease. Consequently, it has been used in breeding programmes with growers seeking to marry its unique flavour with desirable characteristics from other varieties. Some of the well-known varieties derived from Cox's Orange Pippin include Laxton's Superb, Fiesta (Red Pippin) and Kidd's Orange Red. The latter was crossed with Golden Delicious and yielded the well-known Gala. This variety now is a mainstay of supermarket apple selections principally because it is available year round from northern and southern hemisphere suppliers.

The Golden Delicious apple is one of the very few global varieties: it is grown on five continents. It arose as a chance seedling in an apple orchard in Clay County, West Virginia belonging to farmer Anderson Mullins. What first brought it to the attention of Mullins was a bumper crop of yellow apples in an orchard that produced only red apples. Then he discovered that the apple would keep fresh and crisp until late spring. At this time, Mullins was buying his fruit trees from Stark Brothers Nursery in Missouri. Figuring that they might be interested in his new apple variety he sent them samples of the fruit in 1914. Stark Brothers paid $10,000 for exclusive access to the tree and quickly grafted scions to their rooting stock in Missouri. Hoping to capitalize on a comparison with the popular Red Delicious, another Stark apple, the new variety was called Golden Delicious. Today, its heavy cropping and long keeping quality make it popular with supermarket suppliers even if it is not to the taste of consumers.

Many British consumers think that the Golden Delicious is a French apple and would be surprised to know that it is American. They also think that the Granny Smith is a British apple whereas it is not. However, Granny Smith herself was English having been born Maria Ann Sherwood in Peasmarsh, Sussex. She married Thomas Smith, a farm labourer, and in 1838 they emigrated to Australia. The Smiths took up residence in Ryde, near Sydney, a district that had a reputation for fruit growing. According to a record kept by the Smith family, Maria had cooked some French crab apples from Tasmania but saved the seeds which subsequently she planted in her garden. One of the resulting seedlings developed into a tree that produced a green but sweet apple with a greasy skin, obviously the result of a chance cross with what is believed to be a Cleopatra apple. When Maria Smith died in 1870 her apple was cultivated only in local orchards. It was another 25 years before the New South Wales Department of Agriculture initiated large scale cultivation of 'Granny Smith's Seedling' and declared it a suitable variety for export.

Despite the existence of very large number of varieties of apples, only a very limited selection can be found in supermarkets regardless of the country in which you live. This is because supermarket buyers want apples that are free of skin blemishes and uniform in size, shape and colour. They also want ones that keep well and can survive the rigours of international transport. By and large, flavour and aroma come low down on the selection criteria. In the UK, the apple varieties that meet the needs of supermarkets are Red Delicious, Golden Delicious, Gala, Granny Smith and Braeburn. Of these, the Braeburn probably has the best flavour: the others tend to be very sweet.

Even when a supermarket stocks an apple variety that you like there is no guarantee that it will taste as good as it should. Most apples reach their peak taste about three months after picking yet it is not unusual to see much older apples on sale. Around April/May and September/October Gala apples from both northern and southern hemispheres can be found in supermarkets at the same time. Clearly, one lot has spent six months in storage. The weather and soil type also influence flavour so, if you are prepared to forego your favourite all year round, get your apples from a farm shop or farmers' market.

Noteworthy Trees

CHAPTER 26

Here We Go Round The Mulberry Bush

The black or common mulberry (*Morus nigra*) is a handsome tree for gardens in southern England and other parts of Britain that are warmed by the Gulf Stream. The trees grow to 20 to 30 feet and have a spreading head of branches clothed with large-lobed leaves. Mature specimens produce dark red berries that are extremely juicy and have a very refreshing taste. Since these berries do not keep well, even in the refrigerator, they are seldom sold in shops and anyone presented with them can be confident that they truly are fresh.

The black mulberry is mentioned by many of the early Greek and Roman writers and so has been known in southern Europe from the earliest times even though it probably was introduced from Persia (Iran). Ovid in his *Metamorphoses* refers to the legend of Pyramus and Thisbe, who were slain beneath its shade whence their blood turned the fruit from white to red. Virgil described the tree as *sanguinea morus* and Pliny the Elder described its use in medicine. Confirmation that they are describing the mulberry comes from mosaics excavated from the ruins at Pompeii. The mulberry has a reputation for being the last tree to come into leaf and according to old gardeners 'When mulberry trees are green, no more frosts are seen'. This merely echoes the words of Pliny who wrote:

> Of all the cultivated trees, the Mulberry is the last that buds, which it never does till the cold weather is past, and it is therefore called the wisest of trees.

It is thought that the mulberry was introduced to Britain by the Romans, possibly as a source of fruit for their troops. The earliest reference to mulberries in England is in documentation produced following the murder of Thomas Beckett in Canterbury Cathedral in 1170. Apparently, Henry II having asked 'Who will rid me of this troublesome priest' then was filled with remorse at the Archbishop's violent death. He ordered an inquiry and it transpired that the four knights who were responsible for the deed had changed into their armour under a mulberry tree.

The last place that William Shakespeare lived in Stratford upon Avon was New Place in Chapel Street. In the garden there was a mulberry tree thought to have been planted by Shakespeare himself. After the death in 1623 of Shakespeare's wife Anne, the house passed into the ownership of the Clopton family. They followed the aristocratic tradition of opening grand houses to the public (and hence tourist attractions are nothing new!). However, the next owner was the Reverend Francis Gastrell and he objected to the constant stream of onlookers. One night, in a fit of fury, he chopped down the mulberry tree and converted it to a pile of logs. The Stratford inhabitants were furious and responded by smashing all the windows of his house. There is a mulberry tree in Kew Gardens that supposedly is derived from a cutting taken from Shakespeare's tree. This seems unlikely as Kew Gardens were not established until much later.

There are a number of famous mulberry trees in England. One mulberry was planted in 1364 in the garden of Draper's Hall, home of one of London's old livery companies. This tree died in 1969 but a cutting taken from it was used to generate its replacement. The oldest mulberry in England is one that was planted in 1548 at Syon House in West London. Another old mulberry is a 400-year-old one that can be found in the gardens of Buckingham Palace. This is the only surviving member in the gardens of a group of them planted at the behest of James I (James VI of Scotland) who reigned from 1603–1625. Other specimens planted at the same time can be found in the Westminster – St James area of London.

James I was a bit of a fetishist about silk clothes. In the 17th century, when he came to the throne, silk came from China. In an effort to promote an indigenous silkworm industry, he made a decree that mulberry trees were to be established all over the country. It is not known whether planting mulberry trees was his idea or if it was suggested by the Huguenot settlers who ran silk-looms in the Spitalfields area. Either way, mulberry trees were sold to all and sundry for six shillings (30 pence) per hundred. The accounts of Christ's College Cambridge show that they purchased 300 such plants and one of them survives to this day. So taken was James I with the idea of making silk in England that he appointed John Tradescant the Elder as Keeper of His Majesty's Gardens, Vines and Silkworms.

There was only one problem with the proposed establishment of an English silkworm industry. The trees that James I exhorted everyone to plant were black mulberries (*Morus nigra*) but silkworms do not find them particularly palatable. The tree that silkworms normally feed on is the white mulberry (*Morus alba*) and it does not like the damp English climate. However, the trees did have one use that was made famous in the well-known nursery rhyme:

Here we go round the mulberry bush,
The mulberry bush, the mulberry bush,
Here we go round the mulberry bush
At five-o-clock in the morning.

Following the edict of King James, many mulberry trees were planted in prison yards and inmates got their early morning exercise by walking round them.

The Tree That Time Forgot

There is one tree species that has survived on earth little changed for 200 million years, mute witness to the birth and extinction of the dinosaurs, the rise of flowering plants and mammals, and the advance and retreat of ice ages. It is the maidenhair tree (*Ginkgo biloba*), so called because the leaves resemble the pinnae of the maidenhair fern (*Adiantum capillus-veneris*). It is a unique tree because it has no living relatives: it is the only living species of an entire botanical order that already was an ancient group when the first dinosaurs cracked their eggs. Although deciduous and broad-leaved, the ginkgo is not remotely related to other broad-leaved trees for they are angiosperms (flowering plants) that produce their seeds inside an ovary. The ginkgo produces unenclosed seeds and hence belongs to the more primitive gymnosperms (literally 'naked seeds') as do the cycads and conifers.

The earliest ginkgo fossils have been dated to the end of the Permian period, about 240 million years ago (mya). Fossils from the Jurassic period (120 mya) show the existence of ginkgoes similar to those found today. Originally the main competitors of the ginkgo were ferns, tree ferns and cycads but the size, longevity and ability to propagate vegetatively would have given the ginkgo an ecological advantage. Once the flowering plants evolved the ginkgo came under pressure, especially from woody species that are significantly better at colonizing disturbed habitats. The fossil record shows that the ginkgoes decline mirrored the rise of the angiosperms and that they disappeared from North America 7 mya and from Europe 3 mya.

In 1691, a German physician and botanist called Engelbert Kaempfer discovered ginkgo trees in a temple garden in Nagasaki whilst on a mission to Japan for the Dutch East India Company. How had they survived? The first written record of the ginkgo is in Chinese literature from the time of the Sung dynasty (11th century) where it is described as growing south of the Yangtze River. In the first half of the 11th century, Prince Li Wen-Ho moved from southern China to the capital Kaifeng and brought ginkgoes with him. The trees become famous, for the seeds are considered a delicacy, and thenceforth are extensively propagated. The ginkgo is not mentioned in Japanese literature until the end of the 15th century and so it is likely that the trees found by Kaempfer had been raised from seeds brought from China.

Like the Wollemi pine in Australia (chapter 28), the ginkgo may have survived in one or more parts of China because of some unique ecological conditions. The tree can live for more than 1,000 years and this, along with its ability to reproduce vegetatively, would give it some competitive advantage in the battle with angiosperms. Also, the longevity of the tree would have appealed to Buddhists and it is not surprising that old ginkgoes can be found near temples in China, Korea and Japan. However, the most extreme example of the survival of the ginkgo tree against all odds comes from Hiroshima in Japan. Four trees outside a temple in Japan survived the blast from the atomic bomb dropped in 1945, despite being less than one kilometre from the epicentre. Although everything on the surface was completely obliterated, the ginkgo trees re-sprouted without any visible genetic deformation leading the Japanese to call them the 'Bearer of Hope'.

At some point Kaempfer must have brought seeds of the ginkgo back to Holland for there are records of a tree in the Utrecht Botanic Garden in 1734. That tree is still there today. The oldest known ginkgo in Britain is one that was planted in the 1750s on the Duke of Argyll's estate at Twickenham. In 1762 that tree was transported by barge to Kew Gardens where it still flourishes. Now the ginkgo tree is grown all over the temperate world. It is a particular favourite for city plantings, for it tolerates traffic pollution and is largely pest and disease resistant, but it is essential that only male trees are grown!

Ginkgo trees are dioecious; that is, male and female trees are separate. Female trees do not mature sexually until they are about 20 years old and the male trees take even longer. There is no way of sexing trees until they flower and thereby lies a problem. The woody seeds are surrounded by a fleshy seedcoat and when this seedcoat rots the smell is disgusting. Therefore, unless there is good reason to want the seeds, only male trees should be planted and these are best raised from hardwood cuttings. Orientals are much less squeamish about smells than occidentals and to them the seeds are a delicacy as well as being of medicinal value for the treatment of asthma and other respiratory disorders.

In the West, nearly two tonnes of leaves are harvested each year for the manufacture of medicinal products making ginkgo one of the top 10 best-selling herbal remedies. There are many conflicting clinical studies on ginkgo but it is generally recognized that extracts have three effects on the human body: it improves blood flow, it protects against cell damage caused by free radicals (e.g. cancer), and it prevents cardiovascular problems (e.g. heart attacks) caused by platelet aggregation (as does aspirin). The popularity of ginkgo extract is easy to understand. Because it increases blood flow in small capillaries it is the herbal equivalent of Viagra and, if that were not enough, it prevents cancer and heart attacks! Some people also claim that the extracts prevent memory loss and a number of studies suggest that it might be effective in treating Alzheimer's disease. All that is needed is for someone to market ginkgo extracts under the brand name 'Panacea'.

Conservation By Commercialisation

'Living fossil' is a term that was coined by Charles Darwin for any living species of organism which seems to be the same as a species otherwise known only from fossils and has no close living relatives. Some living fossils are species that were known from fossils before living representatives were discovered. Within the plant world the two greatest examples are the dawn redwood (*Metasequoia glyptostroboides*) and the Wollemi Pine. Prior to the discovery of living specimens, the dawn redwood was thought to have been extinct for five million years. Then, in 1941, a forester from the National Central University chanced upon a strange new tree in Szechuan, China. It was *M. glyptostroboides*. At the time of its discovery, China was torn by war and it was 1948 before the first outsiders, a team from Harvard University's Arnold Arboretum, saw a living tree. Today, the dawn redwood is planted widely and is a familiar sight in parks and gardens in the UK and elsewhere.

In 1963 a young Australian called Wayne Harris decided to pursue palynology as a career. 'Palynology is the study of …' is the kind of question you expect to get on 'Who wants to be a Millionaire' and the answer is fossil pollen. Harris began examining sediments from the Otway basin in the state of Victoria that were 45 million years old. One kind of pollen appeared in all of Harris's samples but failed to match anything in the scientific literature. He called this strange new pollen *Dilwynites*. Subsequent studies showed that *Dilwynites* was present in Australia 90 million years ago, appeared in New Zealand about 70 million years ago and in Antarctica about 50 million years ago. The occurrence of *Dilwynites* started to decline about 35 million years ago, coinciding with dramatic global cooling and Australia's continental drift northwards into drier latitudes. The most recent known *Dilwynites* was recorded in sediments from the Australian Bass Strait that are two million years old – until the discovery of the Wollemi Pine.

On 10 September 1994, almost 30 years after Harris discovered *Dilwynites*, a group of three men set out to explore part of the wilderness area that constitutes Australia's Wollemi National Park. The leader of the group was David Noble, a field officer with the National Parks and Wildlife Service of New South Wales. After abseiling down into one narrow canyon, Noble noticed a stand of large, peculiar trees. He collected a few leafy twigs from these unusual but distinctive trees and showed them to colleagues on his return. None of those consulted recognized them so Noble returned to Wollemi to photograph the trees and collect leaves, bark and fertile material that would enable a precise identification. Eventually it was realized that this new tree belonged to the family Araucariaceae.

The family Araucariaceae contained just two genera, *Araucaria* and *Agathis*, and many of the species are botanical hermits that grow in fragmented populations. For example, the Monkey Puzzle tree (*Araucaria araucana*) is native only to a small part of Chile. The Norfolk Island pine (*Araucaria heterophylla*) is native to tiny Norfolk Island and the New Zealand Kauri (*Agathis australis*) to a small part of New Zealand's North Island. The tree discovered by Noble was another hermit and also a new genus. In choosing a name for this new tree it was decided to commemorate the Wollemi wilderness and David Noble. In botany, the genus is always a Latin noun of the feminine gender and so the tree became *Wollemia*. In honouring Noble the specific epithet should have been *noblei*. However, it was feared that this might be trivialized and the tree known as the 'nobbly pine'. To prevent this, the species name was changed to *nobilis*, the Latin adjective meaning 'noble'. Thus the tree discovered by Noble became known to botanists as *Wollemia nobilis* and to the general public as the Wollemi Pine, even though botanically it is not a pine tree. Eventually the palynologists realized that their *Dilwynites* was none other than *Wollemia* and so another living fossil was identified.

When the discovery of the Wollemi Pine became public knowledge the press reported it as the 'tree from the age of the dinosaurs' thereby conjuring up an image of Arthur Conan Doyle's *Lost World.* The mystique was enhanced by the cloak of secrecy thrown around the precise location of the trees. Those people who were permitted to see the tree in the wild but who were not involved in its conservation were blindfolded before being flown in by helicopter. There were good reasons for the secrecy. The group of Wollemi Pine discovered by Noble numbered only about 24 trees and rumours quickly circulated that conifer collectors were prepared to spend large sums of money to obtain specimens. Furthermore, the site was in an area of sandy loam on a steep slope and was vulnerable to damage by human feet. Since the original discovery of the Wollemi Pine two more stands have been discovered nearby. One group of 10 trees was found in 1995 and another group of three trees in 2000. The delay in finding the second and third groups, despite much searching by the Parks Service, attests to the density of vegetation and the inhospitable terrain wherein they reside.

In 1996 another threat to the Wollemi Pine was discovered that justified attempts to keep their location secret. Analysis of the different trees showed that they were genetically identical. This lack of variability, coupled with the susceptibility of many Australian plants to attack by foreign pathogens, made it highly vulnerable to diseases carried by visitors. Indeed, in experiments conducted at the Sydney botanical gardens, seedlings of the Wollemi Pine were found to be highly susceptible to many common fungi. To counter this threat and ensure the conservation of the Wollemi Pine the New South Wales government developed an unusual strategy: everyone who wanted a specimen could have one – for a price! A company called Wollemi Australia was established and it has the rights to propagate the plant on a commercial scale and market it internationally. In 2006 it was possible to buy juvenile specimens of the Wollemi Pine in Australia and the UK. It will not suit everyone's garden as it grows to 100 feet and tends to shed whole branches rather than individual leaves. Nevertheless, *Wollemia nobilis* may be transformed from one of the rarest plants on Earth to one of the most widespread ornamentals in temperate and subtropical regions – an example of conservation through commercialization!

Roses And Orchids

The Queen Of Flowers

For reasons that I do not understand, gardening magazines regularly conduct surveys to find the identity of their readers' favourite flower. The answer always is the same: the rose. Had such surveys been conducted 3,000 years ago the answer probably would have been the same. Greek mythology is full of stories about the origins of the rose and how the spilling of blood accounts for its red colour. The following words, wrongly ascribed to the Greek muse Sapphos, tell of the rose's popularity:

Would Jove appoint some flower to reign
In matchless beauty on the plain,
The rose (all mankind will agree)
The rose the Queen of flowers shall be!
Its beauty charms the Gods above,
Its fragrance is the breath of love …

The roses that people grow in their gardens today are the result of over 100 years of intensive breeding and are quite different from the species roses with which the ancient Greeks and Romans were familiar. So, what is the universal appeal? Is it the tantalising scent, the exquisite symmetry of form or the varied and beautiful colours?

The earliest human record of roses is a 3,500 year-old fresco that now resides in the museum in Herakleion in Crete. It depicts a rose known as the Holy Rose that goes by the botanical name *Rosa x richardii.* It is not a wild rose but a hybrid of *R. gallica*, a species that grows wild throughout the Mediterranean region and whose genes are in all modern roses. In the 8th century BCE Homer wrote *The Iliad* and *The Odyssey* and these contain references to the use of rose oil. In the latter there is a description of the splendid palace of King Nestor of Pylos, one of the heroes of Troy. Archaeologists examining the ruins of this palace have found clay tablets inscribed with large inventories of rose-scented oil. Given that it takes 15 rose flowers to make one drop of rose oil, roses must have been cultivated on a grand scale. Ancient tablets also tell of roses being grown in the gardens of King Midas, he of the golden touch, near Ankara in 700 BCE.

The Old Testament was written about the same time as Homer's classic texts. Although it contains many references to roses, most of the descriptions are of flowers quite unrelated to the genus *Rosa.* One description of what could be a true rose appears in a description of the Promised Land in the Second Book of Esdras: '…seven mighty mountains, on which grow roses and lilies, whereby I will fill thy children with joy'. This could be the strongly-scented shrubby species known as *R. phoenicia* that grows at high elevations in the Holy Land.

Theophrastus (372–286 BCE) was a favourite pupil of Aristotle and in his text *Enquiry into Plants* he provides the first written description of the basic principles of good rose cultivation. In order to improve the quality of flowers the bushes should be pruned regularly and provided with manure. He also recommended that roses be propagated from cuttings and by grafting.

Like the Greeks, the Romans were great fans of roses. Much of our information about their horticultural practices comes from the writings of such luminaries as Virgil (70–1 BCE) and Pliny the Elder (23–79 CE). In their time the centre of rose growing was Paestum, a city about 50 miles south of Naples, and the farmers there were relatively sophisticated. They were able to force roses into bloom out of season by cultivating them in frames heated by the decay of fresh horse manure. Pompeii, which is close to Naples and Paestum, was famous for its roses and today in the remains you can find frescos that include roses. From these reproductions, and the writings of Pliny the Elder, it is possible to recognize *R. alba*, *R. canina* (the Dog rose) and the Rose of Miletus. The latter has petals that have the unusual property of being more fragrant when dry than when fresh. These petals were highly prized for cooking, perfumery and medicine for they were available all the year round. The Rose of Miletus probably is the same as the Apothecary's Rose whose botanical name is *R. gallica* 'Officinalis'. Incidentally, Pliny died from inhalation of toxic fumes whilst watching the eruption of Vesuvius that destroyed Pompeii.

The Romans used roses in many ways. Julius Caesar is credited with starting the fashion of wearing rose garlands on the head, supposedly to hide his baldness. The wealthy scattered rose petals in their baths and anointed themselves with rose oil. They also reclined on pillows or mattresses stuffed with rose petals and this is the origin of the phrase 'a bed of roses'. At one notorious party, Heliogabalus had so many rose petals dropped from the ceiling that two of his guests suffocated. The Romans also added rose petals to their wine in the belief that it stopped them from getting inebriated; so how did they manage to have a good orgy?

The expression *sub rosa* comes from the Roman practice of hanging a rose over the table in council meetings as a sign that anything said there should not be revealed to others. This was supposed to have been done at banquets as well but if events got out of hand and an orgy ensued it is unlikely that anyone could remember anything, rose or no rose. The practice derived from the myth that Cupid once offered a rose to Harpocrates, the god of silence, to hush up some *faux pas* committed by his mother Venus. Much later, the concept of discussions being *sub rosa* was adopted by the Catholic church and roses were hung over the confessionals in some churches. One can still be seen in Worms cathedral in Germany. Today, the practice of hanging a rose above the table has been stylised into that familiar modern household fitting, the ceiling rose.

Many people today would not consider giving someone a gift of flowers containing a mixture of red and white flowers. Nurses in particular feel that such a combination is unlucky because they say it reminds them of death and blood. However, the superstition is nothing new. Pious Romans used to adorn the tombs of their loved ones with mixtures of red and white roses and you never gave the living what you gave to the dead!

Legends Galore: Old Roses In Europe

As noted elsewhere (chapter 29), roses were an essential component of high living in ancient Rome. After the fall of the Roman Empire, the growth of roses for pleasure was discontinued although some roses would have been maintained in monastery gardens for medicinal purposes. During the 12th and 13th centuries, armies of Christian soldiers from all over Europe descended on the Holy Land with the object of wresting control of it from the Muslims. These crusaders would have encountered roses for the rose was the favourite flower of Islam and roses were supposed to have sprung from the sweat of the Prophet. Legend has it that they brought roses back to France, Germany and England but, given that the Crusades ended in disarray, this seems unlikely.

Another rose legend concerns Henry II (1133–1189) who had a mistress named Rosamund (*aka* Jane Clifford). Henry hid her in a labyrinth at Woodstock near Oxford but she was tracked down and murdered by Henry's wife, Eleanor of Aquitaine. A new rose with red and white stripes sprouted on the site of Rosamund's death and this acquired the name *Rosa mundi*. Rose breeders consider *R. mundi* to be a sport of the Apothecary's rose and it is not uncommon for it to revert.

The Wars of the Roses were a series of civil wars fought in medieval England from 1455 to 1487 between adherents of the House of Lancaster and the House of York. Both houses were branches of the Plantagenets and were descendants of Henry III. The name 'Wars of the Roses' had its origin in the badges associated with the two royal houses: the red rose of Lancaster (Apothecary's rose, *R. gallica* 'Officinalis') and the white rose of York (*R. alba* 'Semi Plena'). However, the name was not used at the time but came into common use in the 16th century as a result of a fictional scene in Shakespeare's Henry VI part I. According to Shakespeare, the Wars began following a quarrel in the rose garden of the Temple church in London. In true theatrical fashion, the various noblemen pluck a red or white rose to show their allegiance whilst the Earl of Warwick despairingly says:

And here I prophesy: this brawl today,
Grown to this faction in the Temple garden,
Shall send between the red rose and the white
A thousand souls to death and deadly night.

The Wars of the Roses effectively ended after the victory of Henry Tudor at the Battle of Bosworth in 1485. He became Henry VII and strengthened his position by marrying Elizabeth of York. To commemorate the peace, heralds created the most famous rose of all: the Tudor rose. This consists of a white rose superimposed on a red one. Although still the badge of England it has no counterpart in real life. There is a rose known as the York and Lancaster Rose but it does not resemble the Tudor rose and was not created until the 17th century. The oldest authenticated image of an individual in the National Portrait Gallery is one of Henry VII and in it he is holding a rose in his right hand – a red rose!

During the 16th and 17th centuries, numerous plant books were published. From the descriptions in them it is clear that an impressive variety of roses was available to gardeners. In addition to the roses mentioned above, there were the Damask roses that got their name because they were supposed to come from Damascus. The original Summer Damask (*R. x damascena*) is believed to be a natural hybrid between *R. gallica* and *R. phoenicea* and probably originated in Syria. Whereas the Summer Damasks flower once a year, the Autumn Damasks (*R. x bifera*) flower twice a year and are the result of a cross between *R. gallica* and the Musk rose *R. moschata*. Another species rose that was available was the yellow *R. foetida* that later would play a part in the breeding of new varieties. This rose was native to Persia (Iran) and there is reference to it Omar Khayyam's *Rubaiyat*. Since it came to England via Austria it is known as the Austrian rose.

Attar of roses is a highly perfumed extract of roses. It takes over a million petals to produce one litre of attar but this attar is so concentrated that one drop will perfume 10 litres of eau de cologne. The centre for attar production is the Valley of the Roses in Bulgaria where they grow one particular cultivar of *R. x damascena*, 'Trighintipetala' otherwise known as the Kazanlik rose. In the 16th century, French perfumers and apothecaries exhibited the protectionism for which the French are still famous and claimed that attar derived from the red Rose of Provins (*aka* the Apothecary's rose) was superior. Today, the French perfume industry makes its attar from the pink *R. x centifolia*, a hybrid of an Alba and the Autumn Damask. *R. x centifolia* has a number of common names including Rose of Provence and the Great Holland Rose. Some time in the 18th century, a sport of *R. x centifolia* arose in which the scent glands on the backs of the sepals are exaggerated into growths that look like moss. This sport is known as *R. x centifolia* 'Muscosa' or the Moss Rose.

All of the roses described above have one particular undesirable characteristic: they flower for only a short period. This is because they flower at the ends of their shoots. Plants such as petunias that flower all summer long bear flowers in the axils of their leaves and this allows them to grow and bloom simultaneously for months on end. Modern roses supposedly flower perpetually from spring until autumn but in reality the flowers appear in successive waves or flushes. This property derives from the China Rose. Originally called *R. indica* it is known now as *R. chinensis*. It is not clear how this rose came to Europe but it possibly was brought back from China by Peter Osbeck, a pupil of Carl Linnaeus (see chapter 1). However it arrived, it was a key to modern rose breeding.

A lady by the name of Marie-Josephe-Rose Tascher de la Pagerie was born in Martinique in 1763 to a family of sugar planters. She moved to Paris and married a nobleman who lost his head in the French Revolution. She then married the most powerful man in Europe, Napoleon Bonaparte, and acquired the name Josephine. She also acquired a property known as Malmaison where she cultivated hundreds of plants new to France. Josephine loved roses and developed the first dedicated rose garden that by the time of her death in 1814 had more than 250 different varieties. A number of these varieties were to play an important role in the development of modern roses and we know of them because she had her favourite painter, Pierre-Joseph Redoute paint them all.

Josephine grew the Gallicas, Damasks, Albas, Centifolias and the Moss roses as well as three important China roses. Two of these were 'Old Blush' and 'Slater's Crimson China'. A third was a rose that Redoute called *R. indica fragrans* 'Humes Blush'. The story of how Josephine acquired this rose is amazing. During the Napoleonic Wars the British Navy blockaded the French ports but the Prince Regent made an order that plants destined for Josephine were to be given free passage. At the time, her gardener at Malmaison was a Scot and he brought her 'Humes Blush' from England. The important feature of this rose is that its flowers have a smell reminiscent of Chinese-grown China tea, but not Indian or Sri Lankan tea. It was the first of the Tea-scented or Tea roses. After Josephine's death another Tea rose called 'Park's Yellow' was added to the collection. These four roses – 'Old Blush', Slater's Crimson China', 'Humes Blush' and 'Park's Yellow – now are known as the 'Four Stud Chinas' because they are the ancestors of all today's repeat blooming roses.

Today, there is nothing left of Josephine's great rose collection at Malmaison but Redoute's work lives on. His paintings have been reproduced again and again over the years, and in many forms, as the following rhyme makes clear:

Napoleon and Josephine
They both sat down to dine;
Their table was set splendidly;
They had the best of wine.
But something marred the picture
And left it incomplete;

They really needed table mats
In front of every seat.
'I have an inspiration!'
They both cried out in chorus,
'We'll send for old Redoute,
And he will paint some for us.'

The anonymous writer of this little rhyme conveniently forgot that by the time Josephine engaged Redoute she had been separated from Napoleon for a number of years. Still, it makes a nice story.

One legacy of Josephine's birth on a sugar plantation was blackened and rotting teeth. Although Josephine managed to attract many lovers in addition to her two husbands, it is said that she was so embarrassed by her teeth that she always tried to hide them with a posy of roses. Perhaps her teeth were the origin of the apocryphal phrase 'Not tonight, Josephine'!

'Simply The Rose, Perfect In Every Moment Of Its Existence'

This essay is about the breeding of modern roses hence the use of the quotation from Ralph Waldo Emerson for the title. In the 19th century France, and not England, was the centre of rose breeding. The breeders, mostly centred round Lyon, crossed the old Spring-flowering roses that had been grown in Europe for centuries with the new oriental perpetual-flowering roses (chapter 30). The products of these crosses were known as Hybrid Perpetuals. In reality, they were not perpetually flowering but repeat-flowering hybrids that the French describe as '*remontant*'.

In 1867, Empress Eugenie promoted a competition to breed a new rose that would be called 'La France' and that would bring fame and fortune to the winner. The prize went to Jean-Baptiste Guillot of Lyon for a pink rose that combined the splendour and cold-hardiness of the Hybrid Perpetuals with the compactness and continuous flowering of the Tea roses. 'La France' became the first in a new group of roses that are known today as Hybrid Tea roses and all roses bred since 1867 are considered to be Modern Roses. Later, Hybrid Tea roses were improved by crossing them with the yellow species *R. foetida*. The progeny of these crosses had glossier leaves, increased resistance to mildew and brighter and newer colours.

A few years after the creation 'La France', two new roses arrived in

France from Japan. The first of these was *R. rugosa*, a dense shrubby species with disease resistance, a sweet scent, a spectacular display of hips in late summer and autumn and, most important, seldom out of flower. The second was *R. multiflora*, a climber with sprays of double flowers. At his nursery in Lyon, Guillot crossed *R. multiflora* with *R. chinensis* to produce the low growing, ever-blooming roses known as Polyantha Roses (*polyantha* = many-flowered). Crossing the Polyantha roses with Hybrid Tea roses produced the class of roses known today as Floribundas. As the name suggests, they produce an abundance of flowers and this makes them favourites with landscape gardeners but they have no scent.

Another talented French rose breeder was Francis Meilland. In the 1930s he bred a stunning Hybrid Tea rose with very large flowers and a light yellow to cream colour. At the outbreak of the Second World War he sent cuttings to friends in various countries so that it would be preserved. In 1945 Meilland wrote to Field Marshal Alan Brooke to thank him for his key part in the liberation of France and to ask if he could name his new rose after him. Brooke declined the honour but suggested that an appropriate name would be 'Peace'. The adoption of the name 'Peace' was formally announced on the day that Berlin fell to the allies. Later that year, Peace roses were given to all the delegates at the inaugural meeting of the United Nations in San Francisco with a note that read 'we hope the 'Peace' rose will influence men's thoughts for everlasting world peace.

After the Second World War, rose breeding took off in Britain and a number of breeders acquired international fame. One such breeder was Sam McGredy, the fourth member of the family to bear that name. The first Sam McGredy started a nursery in Northern Ireland hybridizing pansies. The second began hybridizing roses and won so many prizes that he was dubbed 'The Irish Wizard'. The third continued the practice of breeding roses and his 'Rubaiyat' was the All-American Rose winner in 1947. The fourth Sam McGredy is best known for the introduction of 'hand painted' roses. These have one colour striped or splashed with another and the first was named after Pablo Picasso.

There is an interesting story around the naming of the rose 'Picasso'. Because McGredy wanted to patent it so that he could collect royalties, he needed to get permission from Picasso to use his name. He got a letter from Picasso's agent saying that it was all right to use the name. The Patent Office did not accept this letter because it was not signed by Picasso himself. So, McGredy wrote again asking for a letter signed by Picasso himself. In return he got a scathing letter from Picasso's agent pointing out that the great artist never signed anything himself because his autograph sold for over $10,000 (in 1970). Eventually the Patent Office accepted the letter from Picasso's agent.

McGredy's top selling rose in America is one called 'Olympiad'. It is a red Hybrid Tea rose named for the Los Angeles Olympic Games. It was the only rose used in landscaping the games area and all medal winners were presented with a single bloom of it. When selecting new roses McGredy looks for colour, vigour, number of blooms per bush and life as a cut flower. He does not worry about fragrance because of the connection between restored fragrance and tendency to mildew. A completely different approach has been taken by another famous rose breeder, David Austin. He set out to produce a scented rose with rosette-shaped or cupped flowers with the emphasis on charm and beauty rather than sheer brilliance of colour. When he started he was totally out of line with the trends of the day but today his roses are famous and known simply as 'English roses'.

It is obvious that the floral characteristics of a new rose will have a major influence on its public appeal. Less obvious, but just as important, is the choice of name. The roses bred by David Austin are named after famous English people, events and landmarks. His first new rose was named 'Constance Spry' in honour of the renowned flower arranger and cook. Six years later he introduced a series of repeat-flowering varieties including 'Wife of Bath' and 'Canterbury' in commemoration of Chaucer. Other new varieties have been named 'Shakespeare', 'Mary Rose' (after Henry VIII's flagship), 'Darcy Bussel' and 'Lady Emma Hamilton'. In 2006, television viewers in Britain by a huge margin voted his 'Gertrude Jekyll' as Britain's favourite rose – a fitting honour for a famous rose breeder and a famous English plantswoman.

Not Just A Pretty Face

Of all the hundreds of thousands of flowering plants in the world the rose is by far the most popular. When gardeners speak of roses it is not long before one hears the phrase 'Queen of Flowers'. There is no flower that presents itself to its admirers in so many different forms as the rose. Because of its appeal, breeders have crossed varieties from the Middle East, China and elsewhere and selected the offspring with the most pleasing floral arrangements and colours. Ask most people about the value of roses and they will comment on the visual pleasure that they bring or possibly their exquisite scent. Few, however, will think of their commercial value other than as ornamental plants.

According to Confucius, the great Chinese philosopher of the fifth century BCE, the Emperor of China had in his library 600 books concerning the culture of roses. It is hard to imagine that there were that many authors of books, let alone books on roses, at this time but there is no doubt that roses were important to the Emperor. Oil of roses was extracted from the plants growing in his gardens but its use was highly restricted. Only nobles and dignitaries of the court could use rose oil: any commoners found in possession of it were condemned to death. This rose oil probably was quite different from the rose oil of today in that it was not distilled from the petals. Rather, the method of preserving the aroma was to steep the petals in vegetable oil or to extract it with a fatty oil to make pomade. An alternative was to make a water infusion. Although credit for the process of infusion is given to the 10th century physician Avicenna it is likely that it was developed much earlier.

The idea that rose oil can be extracted by steam distillation can be traced back to Persia at the end of the 16th century. For the wedding of the Princess Nour-Djihan with the Emperor Djihanguyr, a canal circling the palace gardens was dug and filled with rose petals and water. As the water was heated by the sun an oily film formed on the surface. When this was skimmed off it was found to have an exquisite perfume. Over the next 100 years the process of distillation was developed and around the city of Shiraz the production of Persian Otto (Attar of Roses) became big business. According to the German physician Engelbrecht Kaempfer (chapter 27), who spent 10 years (1683–1693) travelling through Persia and South-East Asia, it even was exported to countries such as India where it was used for flavouring food. Today, Iran does not even produce rose oil for its own use.

Ottoman (Turkish) merchants were responsible for spreading the cultivation of the Damask rose (*Rosa damascena*) throughout the Balkans. One valley in Bulgaria provided the perfect environment for growing roses and eventually became the finest rose oil producing region in the world. A nearby town became known as Kazanlik: 'kazan' is the Turkish word for 'still' and Kazanlik literally means 'the place of stills'. Throughout the 19th and early 20th centuries Bulgaria monopolised the supply of rose oil. Dramatic changes in the political and economic climate in Bulgaria after World War II led to a steady decline in the industry and Turkey became the dominant producer.

The scent of roses is at its greatest just as the flowers begin to open. This happens in late May and lasts anywhere from two to four weeks. Harvesting occurs during this period and begins each day at sunrise and is completed by 10am before the heat of the sun can evaporate the oil. In Bulgaria it was common practice for the rose oil to be distilled on site using direct-fire stills operated by the farmers themselves. Although primitive, these could produce one kilo of oil from 2,500 kilos of rose flowers, a higher figure than can be achieved with modern industrial distillation techniques! A small amount of rose oil has been produced around the town of Grasse in the south of France since before the Revolution. Unlike the Bulgarians, the French use the cabbage rose (*R. centifolia*) for oil production. This does not have the body of the Bulgarian oil and so new hybrids are being developed where odour and not appearance is the characteristic being sought.

The amount of oil made by roses is strongly influenced by the weather. So too is its exact composition, and hence its quality and the price it can command. Not surprisingly, some unscrupulous suppliers 'extend' the rose oil by diluting it with geranium (*Pelargonium graveolens*) or palmarosa (*Cymbopogon martini*) oil. Both these oils are rich in geraniol, the main constituent of rose oil. A different approach to changing the composition of rose oil was used by the company International Flavours & Fragrances. They sent a rose called Overnight Scentsation on a space shuttle flight to see if lack of gravity changed its scent. It did, and the new scent has been incorporated into a perfume by Shiseido called Zen for Women (as if men would use it!).

Rose water is a by-product of Bulgarian rose oil manufacture. Although of little culinary importance in Europe, rose water is an important flavouring in the Middle East and Asia. It is an essential component of marzipan and many sweet dishes such as Turkish Delight. Turks dissolve some *locoum*, a very sweet confectionery with a rose fragrance, in their coffee and in Iran they eat rose-flavoured honey and jam. Rose ice cream is known in many Middle Eastern countries and in Northern India there are rose-flavoured drinks and desserts.

It is not just rose water that has culinary uses; rose hips have been used for centuries as a form of fruit and as an important source of vitamin C. Native North Americans prized them as a source of food especially as they could be dried and kept for use throughout the winter. In mediaeval Britain they were used in a similar way as the herbalist Gerard tells us 'the fruit when it is ripe maketh the most pleasante meats and banketting dishes as tartes and such-like'. Strictly speaking, rose hips are false fruits because they are formed by the end of the stalk growing up and around the carpels and enclosing them as a case. The real fruits, each containing one seed, are the little hairy objects within the hips. One of the most prolific producers of hips is the dog rose (*Rosa canina*) and this was grown commercially for the production of rose hip syrup, an old-fashioned remedy rich in vitamin C. During World War II, British people were encouraged to harvest rose hips and use them as nutritional supplements. Many different recipes for their use were available and most called for the removal of the hairy fibres covering the seeds. In the wartime spirit of wasting nothing, boys found that these fibres made a wonderful 'itching powder' with which to annoy their friends!

Avid growers of roses will know that they are prone to a variety of diseases such as blackspot, rust and mildew. In some parts of the world, such as Australia, they have turned this susceptibility to advantage. Winemakers plant roses at the end of each row of vines as 'indicator plants'. These are the botanical equivalent of taking a canary down a mine. When the roses start getting diseased it is time to spray the vines. As someone who is not a fan of roses but a lover of wine, I can think of no greater sacrifice!

Those Deceitful Orchids

Orchids are the largest and most varied of the flowering plants and are renowned for their spectacular floral diversity. The complex structural variations of orchid flowers have attracted evolutionary biologists and gardeners alike. Basically, orchid flowers are zygomorphic: that is, they are divisible into two identical halves but only along one plane. They have three outer sepals and three inner petals. The sepals often are differentiated into a large and showy medial sepal that is flanked by two lateral sepals. Similarly, two lateral petals flank the greatly enlarged third petal or labellum. The labellum is particularly important as it often serves as a landing platform for pollinators.

Unlike other flowering plants orchids have no stamens with free filaments (male reproductive organs). Instead, the male and female reproductive organs are fused into a single structure known as the column that is located in the centre of the flower. At the top of the column is the anther and at the bottom the sticky stigma (female organ). The rostellum, a beak-like structure separates the male and female organs and acts as a barrier to prevent self pollination. Another unique feature of orchid flowers is that the pollen grains stick together to form pollinia that are attached to a sticky structure to form a pollinarium. It is this pollinarium, rather than individual pollen grains, that gets attached to insects that visit orchid flowers.

Many plants are pollinated by insects and the plants ensure that this happens by making their flowers as attractive as possible to the insects. This they do by various means including the production of a sugar-rich liquid called nectar. Essentially, this nectar is a reward for visiting the flower but, in order to get it, the insect has to brush past the flower's reproductive structures. Orchids are unusual in that they have evolved in such a way that they can only be pollinated by a single species of insect. A good example is the Madagascar Star Orchid (*Angraecum sesquipedale*) or 'Darwin's orchid'. This orchid has evolved an incredibly long nectar spur that forces the hawk moths that pollinate it to rub their faces on the pollinaria as they reach for the nectar. In response to the difficulty in reaching the nectar, the moths over time evolved longer and longer tongues. But, if the moth has a long tongue it can reach the nectar without touching the pollinaria. Consequently, the orchid has to evolve longer and longer spurs to force the moth to pollinate it.

The co-evolutionary process described above has been taken to extremes in the Madagascar Star Orchid for its nectar spurs can be as long as 11 inches! When Darwin first encountered this orchid he predicted that a moth would be found that had an equally impressive long tongue. Not surprisingly, his contemporaries thought that he was stupid but 40 years later such a moth was discovered. The hawk moth *Xanthophan morgani praedicta* has a tongue that is 10 inches long and the latter part of its name commemorates Darwin's prediction.

Another example of the close relationship between orchids and insects occurs in the genus *Ophrys*. Two closely related species, *Ophrys fusca* and *O. bilunulata* are specifically pollinated by the bees *Andrena nigroaenea* and *A.flavipes* respectively. The floral scents of the two orchid species are very similar in composition except for one group of compounds known as alkenes. The relative amounts of these alkenes determine which bee visits which orchid.

As well as co-evolving with their pollinators, many orchids are unusual in offering visiting insects no nectar reward whatsoever. This was first reported by Christian Konrad Sprengel in 1793. He called such orchids 'Scheinsaftblumen', sham nectar flowers, and proposed a system of deception that orchids used to attract pollinators. The distinguished naturalist Charles

Darwin wrote a seminal book on orchids entitled *On the various contrivances by which orchids are fertilised by insects.* In this book he confirmed the absence of nectar but stated that he found it incredible that 'bees… should persevere in visiting flower after flower… in the hope of obtaining nectar that is never present'.

There are two types of pollination by deceit: food deception and sexual deception. Food deception involves attracting pollinators by signalling the presence of a food reward but not providing this reward. It occurs occasionally in other flowering plants but never on the grand scale seen with orchids where over one third of species exhibit it. In sexual deception, which is found only in orchids, the flower attracts male pollinators by mimicking the mating signals of the female. Why so many orchids exhibit pollination by deceit is a bit of a mystery for the energy saved by not making nectar is insignificant. What is known is that insects spend significantly less time visiting flowers where there is no reward compared with flowers that produce nectar. Furthermore, pollinators foraging in a patch of rewarding plants tend to visit neighbouring plants whereas deceived pollinators often leave the patch immediately. This greatly increases the frequency of out-breeding and enhances survival of the orchid.

The best known example of sexual deception occurs in the Eurasian orchids belonging to the genus *Ophrys.* Some species, such as the Bumblebee Orchid (*Ophrys bombyliflora*) look and smell so much like female bumblebees that male bees flying nearby are irresistibly drawn to them and proceed to mate with them. In the process, the pollinarium sticks to the bee's abdomen. When the bee takes flight its movement causes the pollinarium to move its position such that it is ideally placed to slip under the rostellum and come in contact with the stigma of the next orchid visited. Other species of *Ophrys* are mimics of different bees or wasps and also are pollinated by males attempting to mate with the flowers. Clearly, the male wasps and bees get nothing out of the orchid's sexual deception, except possibly frustration, but it may help the females decide which males would make the cleverest mates!

Cites And Sensibility

It is generally recognized that the rose symbolizes love and the lily purity but in thinking about orchids three words come to mind: passion, obsession and sex! No other family of plants appeals to the baser instincts of humans in the way that orchids do. In the 21st century there still are professional plant hunters who go on expeditions where they have to contend with tropical diseases, swarms of insects, venomous snakes, giant spiders and hostile tribesmen – just to collect a single specimen of a single species of orchid. Others will smuggle plants across borders or steal plants from national collections and even go to jail for their efforts. What is it about orchids that drive people to such extreme lengths?

Originating about 120 million years ago, orchids are believed to be one of the earliest flowering plants on earth. Whereas evolution has led to the demise of many other plants, orchids have flourished. Today they are found in every continent except Antarctica and in almost every environment: mountains, bogs, grasslands and rainforests. The largest grows to 44 feet and has six-inch flowers whereas the smallest would fit on a thumbnail. The Orchidaceae also is the largest plant family with over 30,000 species and new ones being discovered almost monthly. In addition, horticulturalists and amateur breeders have generated over 125,000 hybrids.

One of the earliest references to orchids is ascribed to the Chinese philosopher Confucius (551–479 BCE). He compared the orchid flower to a man of noble character and praised its fragrance as 'the scent of king flower'. Another early reference appears in the historical text on plants written by the Greek Theophrastus (370–285 BCE). The name orchid derives from the Greek word for testicles (orchis) and Theophrastus used it to describe a group of plants with paired round tubers.

The orchid also appears in Greek mythology. Orchis was the son of a nymph and the satyr Patellanus. Their union resulted in unbridled passion and excess and their wanton son presided over feasts honouring Priapus, the god representing male procreation. At one celebration, Orchis allowed his hands to wander too freely on one of the priestesses. The gods were outraged and tore him to pieces but the grieving Patellanus managed to transform the remains of his son into orchid flowers. A variation of this myth suggests that the satyrion orchid, now known as *Satyrium*, was the outcome of Patellanus's copulation. The medical term 'satyriasis' has the same derivation and refers to a male's uncontrollable desire for sex.

Orchids had the same effect on Romans as they did on Greeks. In the first century, Pliny the Elder believed that merely holding an orchid tuber would ignite sexual desire. In the 17th century, the Doctrine of Signatures (see chapter 5) stated that the shape and colour of plant parts indicated their medicinal uses. Not surprisingly, orchid tubers were considered testicle analogues so it was thought that they had aphrodisiac properties. The lascivious reputation of orchids continued long after the demise of the Doctrine of Signatures. At the end of the 19th century Marcel Proust wrote a rather complex tale of misguided love entitled *Swann's Way*. In it, Swann offers to fasten an orchid a little more securely in the cleft of his lover's low-necked bodice. He then suggests that he should brush off the pollen from it. We all can guess what follows next!

The phrase 'orchid fever' is used to describe the mania for collecting orchids that swept through 19th century England. William Cattley initiated this orchid fever in 1818 when he succeeded in getting some unpromising plant material to produce huge and outrageously beautiful flowers. These flowers were named *Cattleya labiata* in his honour but, unfortunately, they died shortly thereafter. A search for new specimens was unsuccessful until an orchid enthusiast at a ball in Paris saw one in the cleavage of an ambassadress from South America and traced the plant to Brazil. In 1826 the sixth Duke of Devonshire saw a specimen of *Oncidium papilo* and immediately was hooked on orchids. He commissioned Joseph Paxton to build a greenhouse that was 300 feet long and 150 feet wide so that he could indulge his passion and spent vast sums of money to acquire new specimens. Orchids quickly became highly prized plants for wealthy collectors and owning a greenhouse for growing them was an obvious badge of wealth and worldliness.

Vast numbers of orchid hunters were employed to search all over the world for rare varieties. Theirs was a world of intrigue, suspicion, misinformation, violence and hardship. When hunters returned with new species, if they returned, they seldom admitted where they had found their specimens so that others could not follow their trail. These hunters also were incredibly cavalier. Some sent home orchids literally by the ton because so many would die en route. One expedition to Colombia felled 4,000 trees so that they could collect the orchids from their canopies. The great orchid hunter Wilhelm Micholitz supposedly sent home an orchid growing in a human skull that later was auctioned in London for a huge sum.

Orchid fever lasted for about a century and died out with the start of the First World War. Other than the development of a method for artificial propagation (meristem culture) little happened in the world of orchid growing for 50 years. In the 1960s orchids started to become available in specialist centres and by the 1970s orchids became widely available as cut flowers. This started a new phase of orchid fever except that the afflicted were not wealthy members of the upper classes. Some were wealthy but many others were ordinary members of the community except for their exceptional passion for orchids. Collecting orchids once more was in vogue. Fearing that destruction of orchid habitats on a grand scale was going to recommence, a group of botanical institutions got orchids covered by the Convention on International Trade in Endangered Species of Wild Fauna and Flora (CITES).

If you wish to buy an orchid from overseas then, according to CITES regulations, you need an export permit from your supplier and an import permit for your own country. This is a well-intentioned and reasonable approach and would work well if the enforcement authorities applied common sense. Unfortunately they do not and this has increased the desire for certain plants, raised their market value and led to extensive orchid smuggling. There are a number of cases where national governments have planned large scale destruction of orchid habitats for dams, roads or mining purposes but have then tried to save the plants they get prosecuted for destroying endangered species. CITES and sensibility do not always go together.

Orchids And Ice Cream

Vanilla is one of the world's most expensive flavourings and in the price stakes is beaten only by saffron and cardamom. It is derived from the pods of an orchid, *Vanilla fragrans* (also known as *V. planifolia*), that is native to Mexico and was used by the Aztecs and Mayans of Central America. The pods are harvested just before they ripen but at this stage they have no flavour: they need to be cured for six months. First, they are given a hot water bath and then they are left out in the sun to absorb heat. Each night they are wrapped in blankets and allowed to sweat before being exposed to the sun again. After about 15 days of sweating and drying the principal flavouring compound, vanillin, will have been formed and the pods are left for many more weeks to dry completely. How the Mexican Indians worked all this out is a mystery but they were using vanilla pods to flavour their drinks long before the arrival of the Spanish conquistadores.

In 1519 the Spanish army of Hernando Cortez was conquering Central America with the help of Indian tribes hostile to the Aztecs. At one point Cortez was living with the Aztec leader Montezuma who was being held as a prisoner in his own house. As a consequence he was introduced to a beverage of vanilla flavoured chocolate. When Cortez returned to Europe he took bags of cocoa beans and vanilla pods with him and this new beverage became a favourite with royalty and the rich. Queen Elizabeth I was one of many aficionados. However, in 1602, her apothecary Hugh Morgan suggested that the vanilla pod be used as flavouring in its own right. There-after, vanilla soared in popularity and price and became more popular than any other flavour.

One problem with the popularity of vanilla was that for 300 years it could be sourced only from Mexico. Botanists had shown that it was possible to grow the vanilla orchid in many different countries, and get them to flower, but the plants never bore fruit. Then, in 1836, a Belgian called Charles Morren discovered the cause of the problem. The flowers are pollinated by a tiny bee that is found only in the areas of Mexico where *Vanilla fragrans* is found naturally. No other insects are capable of pollinating the flowers and the bee does not survive outside Mexico.

On the French island of Bourbon (now Reunion) botanist Ferreol Bellier was trying to find a way of pollinating the vanilla orchids that had been introduced by plantation owners. He had no success until 1841 when his 12-year-old slave, Edmond Albius, showed him how to do it. The *Vanilla* flower has a flap, properly known as a rostellum, which separates the male and female parts of the flowers. Albius used a thin stick to lift the flap and his thumb to transfer the pollen to the stigma. This simple method of pollination, still in use today, enabled the island to develop its vanilla industry.

Today, vanilla pods are grown commercially in four different regions of the world. The best vanilla comes from Madagascar and the Indian Ocean islands of Comoro, Reunion and the Seychelles. Indonesia is the second largest producer but its vanilla has a more astringent flavour. Mexico, where the vanilla orchid originated, produces only 10 percent of the global crop. Its vanilla is sweet and spicy. Finally, a small amount of vanilla is produced in Tahiti but this has quite a different flavour as it is derived from a different species, *Vanilla tahitensis*. Should you buy vanilla essence rather than vanilla pods then remember that if it costs little it will not be the genuine product. Much of the vanilla flavouring sold in shops is made from chemically-synthesized vanillin.

Unlike *Vanilla fragrans* which is grown commercially as a source of flavouring, orchids of the genera *Orchis* and *Eulophia* are collected from the wild and used as a source of nutrition. The tubers of these orchids contain a starch-like carbohydrate called bassorin. In Turkey, the Middle East and parts of India the tubers are collected when they are full and fleshy, dried and ground to a powder. This powder is known as salep, literally 'fox testicles', and has long been used to make a wholesome and nutritious drink of the same name.

Although principally a drink of the East, salep was sold in the streets of London before coffee supplanted its use. English salep was available with the best coming from Oxfordshire although most of it was imported from the Middle East. Charles Lamb referred to a salopian shop in Fleet Street and commented that salep made an ideal breakfast for a chimney sweep when accompanied by a slice of bread and butter. Dried salep was an essential item of ship's stores in the days of sailing ships and long voyages because it was so nutritious. One ounce dissolved in two quarts of boiling water was considered sufficient subsistence for each man per day should provisions run short.

In Turkey they use salep for another purpose. They mix it with milk and sugar, freeze it and then beat it with metal rods to produce a form of ice cream known as *dondurma*. This is so stiff it can be eaten with a knife and fork or made into a skipping rope! Dondurma is so popular in Istanbul that one part of the city is known as the 'ice cream district' and regularly jams up with traffic. However, the home of dondurma is the city of Maras that nestles at the base of the Taurus Mountains in south-central Turkey. It has been made here for over 300 years and probably originated when a pot of hot salep froze when stored overnight during the winter. In an attempt to save his valuable material, the vendor probably chipped out the frozen salep with a metal rod. Finding it edible he beat it to a smooth mass and dondurma was born.

Dondurma now is so popular that the wild populations of orchids are under serious threat. It takes 1,000 orchids to produce one kilogramme of salep and this will not make much ice cream. One family firm in Maras uses three tonnes of salep every year, equivalent to twelve million plants, so the total number of plants harvested from the wild is unimaginable.

Although an export ban on salep is in place, the time may be coming when it is not even available in Turkey. People given to indolent enjoyment were once known as lotus-eaters: perhaps we should re-name them orchid eaters!

Fascinating Flowers

Tea, Tarts And Tragedies

Camellias are stars of the winter garden with their waxy blooms of pristine white, candy pink or ruby red set against dark, glossy evergreen foliage. They are native to eastern and southern Asia in an area stretching from the Himalayas to Japan and Indonesia. Camellias have long had decorative uses as they often feature in Japanese and Chinese works of art but horticulturally they are much more important as the source of tea.

There are many legends about the origin of tea but the most popular one ascribes its discovery to the Chinese Emperor Sheng Nung (The Divine Healer) around 2700 BCE. Supposedly, some Camellia leaves were blown by the wind into a pot of hot water from which the Emperor was drinking. The resulting infusion proved so soothing and irresistible that Sheng Nung commended it to all his subjects. Enchanting as this story is, it most likely is no more than a myth. The first written description of tea, or 'Ch'a' as it is known in Chinese, came about 700 CE. Incidentally, the Chinese 'ch'a' may be the origin of the British working class colloquial term 'char'. China enjoyed tea for centuries before it was introduced to the outside world through trade. It is believed that the Turkish Empire got its first taste of tea from a barter trade and thereafter it made its way to Europe. The Portuguese also brought tea back home via Macau, their colony on the southern edge of China.

Tea did not reach England until about 1644 when it became socially important when it was adopted by the court of Charles II. In his diary for 25 September 1661, Samuel Pepys recorded '*I sent for a cup of tea (a China drink) of which I had never drunk before*'. England also was late into the tea trade for the East India Company did not capitalize on tea's popularity until the mid-18th century. The growing demand for tea led to two innovations. The first of these was the introduction of streamlined, tall-masted vessels called clippers that reduced the time from China by two-thirds. The most famous of these tea clippers was the *Cutty Sark* that now is on exhibition in Greenwich. The second innovation was to bring the tea plantations closer to home by establishing them in India and Ceylon (now Sri Lanka). This had another advantage as it avoided the need to pay gold for tea as gold was the only currency that China would accept.

Traditionally, there have been three types of teas: black teas that are fermented and heavily processed, oolong or semi-fermented teas, and green teas which are non-fermented. Recently a new type of tea has been produced, white tea, and it is the Rolls Royce of the tea industry. White tea is made from the same plant as other teas but only the uppermost, most tender leaves are picked and this is done whilst the buds are still covered by fine white hair. This harvesting is done exclusively by gloved hand because white tea never comes in contact with human skin until it reaches your teapot. A typical tea plantation might produce 20 tonnes of black tea in a week but only 20 kilograms of white tea. Not surprisingly, white tea is expensive and costs upwards of £1,000 per kilo. Once English royalty, Russian tsars and Japanese emperors considered white tea as a sign of class but today most white tea goes to the Gulf States and Japan.

In his seminal work *Species Plantarum*, Linnaeus called camellia *Thea sinensis*, i.e. Chinese tea. Later, he renamed it *Camellia sinensis* in honour of Georg Kamel, a Jesuit missionary who studied the flora of the Phillipines. Kamel probably never saw a camellia but the name lives on, albeit with the K in his name changed to a C as there is no letter K in Latin. Whereas *C. sinensis* is cultivated widely for making tea it is *C. japonica* that is the most commonly grown ornamental species. The first camellia plant to be grown in England was shipped there by James Cunningham, an official of the East

India Company. This plant was received in 1739 by Lord Petre of Thorndon Hall in Essex who managed to kill it by growing it in a greenhouse that was too hot. Fortunately, his gardener had taken cuttings which survived. The first double-flowered camellias arrived in England from China in 1792, again courtesy of the East India Company. Fifty years later, the camellia had become a prized ornamental shrub and its cultivation had spread to mainland Europe and North America. In France, it was to play a part in a famous tragedy.

In February 1847, the city of Paris was in mourning because of the death from tuberculosis of La Dame aux Camellias. Her real name was Marie Duplessis. She was one of the most famous French courtesans and much favoured by wealthy men. Her popular name derived from her habit of always carrying a bouquet of camellias. On 25 days of the month they were white. On the remaining five or six days they were red, supposedly to indicate that she was 'indisposed'. In 1844 she began a year-long affair with Alexander Dumas the younger, the illegitimate son of the author of *The Three Musketeers*. Dumas was besotted with Duplessis and shortly after her death wrote the novel *La Dame aux Camelias* that was based on her life.

In *La Dame aux Camelias*, Dumas transforms himself into Armand Duval and Marie Duplessis into Marguerite Gautier. The consumptive Marguerite is the classic tart with the big heart who gives up her young lover Armand, the only man she has ever loved (wishful thinking?), at the behest of his father. The reason for this selfless act is to protect the spotless reputation of the Duval family which is in danger of being destroyed by the scandal of the liaison. The book was exceptionally popular, probably because many people knew of Dumas' affair with Duplessis and read the fiction as fact. Dumas also created a stage version of the story and when first performed in 1852 it was an instant success. Guiseppe Verdi then put the story to music but changed the name of the leading female from Marguerite Gautier to Violetta Valery. The resulting opera is known to music lovers as *La Traviata*. In addition to inspiring *La Traviata*, *La Dame aux Camelias* has been the inspiration for over 20 different motion pictures including *Pretty Woman* and *Moulin Rouge*.

In New Zealand, a white camellia is the symbol of the Suffragists who successfully campaigned for women to have the right to vote. In 1893, a Bill was presented to Parliament to give women the vote and it was passed in the Lower House. The Bill then went to the Legislative Council where the Premier tried to block its passage. In a very visible gesture, women sent white camellias to all members of Parliament who supported suffrage and red camellias to their opponents. What effect this lobbying had on the voting preferences of Council members is not known but the Bill did pass and made New Zealand the first country in the world to grant women political equality.

The single, wild form of the camellia drops its flower heads abruptly, suggesting sudden death. Because of this fragility the camellia has become symbolic of losing one's life and hence it is never given as a gift. In the Far East the camellia is a flower never seen at weddings, only funerals. The late Queen Elizabeth, the Queen Mother, grew camellias in all her gardens. As her body was taken from the Royal Lodge, Windsor to lie in state in the Palace of Westminster, a white camellia from her own gardens was placed on top of the flag-draped coffin. In the Victorian language of flowers, the white camellia denotes unpretending excellence and steadfastness making it a fitting choice for the Queen Mother.

Daft On Dahlias

Dahlias are grown for their striking flower heads. They come in every colour except blue and in a wide variety of forms such as decorative, pompom, cactus, collerette, etc., and can be used for garden display and for cutting. They have one of the longest flowering seasons of any garden flower giving dazzling displays from mid-summer until cut down by frosts. So popular are they that over 20,000 named varieties have been produced in the past 100 years. Thus it is a little surprising to learn that they were first introduced to Europe as a possible food and that when first grown as garden plants they attracted little interest.

Dahlias are native to Mexico and the story of them begins with Aztec mythology. The Aztecs knew the dahlia as *cocoxochitl* and it was a symbol of the Serpent Woman who daily conversed with an eagle who was the messenger of the Gods. One day, when the eagle was relaying messages from the Gods, she found a rabbit sitting beside an agave holding a dahlia in its mouth. This dahlia had eight red flower rays. The Serpent Woman took the dahlia from the rabbit and the Gods told her to impale the flower on the leaves of the agave and hold it to her breast all night long. The next morning she gave birth to Uitzilopochtli, the War God, who was fully armed with the sword-like leaf of the agave. The blood red flower rays had given him a thirst for blood. After that, the Aztecs sacrificed prisoners to the War God every eight years, removing their hearts and placing them on a stone surrounded by dahlias and agave.

In the 16th century the Spanish conquistadors were busy pillaging Central America and often were accompanied by botanists who were charged with bringing back plants from the New World for Spain. One of these botanists was Francisco Hernandez. He spent seven years there from 1571 to 1578. One of his discoveries was the tree dahlia (*D. imperialis*) that has hollow stems and grows to 20 feet or more. The Aztecs often used this as a source of water and gave it the name *acocotli* or 'water cane'. This plant was described and illustrated in Hernadez's book *Thesaurus* but there is no record of it being sent back to Spain.

After Hernandez, dahlias sank back into obscurity for over 200 years until three species were shipped from Mexico to Spain. These were the single red *D. coccinea*, the double purple *D. pinnata* and the delicate single *D. rosea.* Some writers ascribe the introduction of these plants to the naturalist and explorer Friedrich von Humboldt. However, Humboldt did not visit Central and South America until the period 1799– 1804 and yet illustrations of these plants appear in Abbe Cavanille's '*Icones et Descriptiones Plantarum*' of 1791 and 1795! Regardless of when they appeared in Spain, Abbe Cavanille named the plants after the Swedish naturalist, Andreas Dahl, who had been a pupil of the great taxonomist Carl Linnaeus (chapter 1).

An important characteristic of these early dahlias is that they all were hybrids and did not breed true from seed. This quickly led to the appearance of new flower forms and colours. The first double-flowered forms were known as Show and Fancy types. The Show types were self-coloured, ball-like flowers and the Fancy ones were multi-coloured. Soon these dahlias acquired cult status. The Empress Josephine grew them in her famous garden at Malmaison although reputedly she uprooted them after some were stolen by a lady-in-waiting. A botany professor from St Petersburg, Johann Georgi, saw them in Paris and introduced them to Russia and Eastern Europe where they still are known as georginas.

Dahlias arrived in England courtesy of Lady Holland. She and her husband had lived in France and Spain between 1800 and 1805 and sent some back from there to their London home, Holland House, where they flourished. Later, Lord Holland penned the following verse to celebrate 20 years of marriage:

The Dahlia you brought to our isle
Your praises for ever will speak:
Mid gardens as sweet as your smile,
And colour as bright as your cheek.

Many famous people became besotted with dahlias. These included John Wedgwood, founder of the Royal Horticultural Society, who grew over 200 varieties at his property in Staffordshire. The eminent landscape gardener J.C. Loudon wrote that 'they were the most fashionable flower in this country' and Sir Joseph Paxton also wrote enthusiastically about them. Much later they featured in Graham Greene's amusing story, *Travels with My Aunt*, in which a retired bank manager gives up breeding dahlias to go on exotic trips (of both kinds!) with his septuagenarian Aunt Augusta.

During the 19th century numerous new types of dahlia were developed. Anemone-flowered dahlias were discovered in 1829 and in 1850 the first Pompom types were raised in Germany. The latter got their name from the bobble seen on the hats of French sailors. In 1872, a crate of tubers was sent from Mexico to Holland but only one tuber survived the crossing. Fortunately this sole survivor was a new cultivar, subsequently named 'Juarezzii after a President of Mexico, with bright red blooms and rolled back rays. It was used to generate the Cactus and Decorative varieties of dahlias. Finally, the Collerette varieties were developed from a sport that arose at the Jardin Botanique de Lyon. Not content with all these varieties, today's dahlia fanciers are trying to breed ones with blue flowers, with scent and that are frost hardy. Genetic engineering will allow them to do so but will this make them happy? I doubt it.

Given the floral interest in dahlias it is easy to forget that the Aztecs used them as a source of food. The tubers are edible and the Spanish and French experimented with their use as an alternative to potatoes but their taste was not to the liking of European palates. The Aztecs also used the dahlia to treat epilepsy. This we know from the discovery of an amazing book found in the Vatican library in 1931. This book, the *Badianus Herbal*, was compiled in 1552 by Aztec pupils at the Roman Catholic College at Santa Cruz, Mexico. This was 20 years before the discovery of the dahlia by Francisco Hernandez. Given that the book was written in Latin the conquistadores must have done something more beneficial than just looting and pillaging! Europeans and North Americans found another use for the dahlia. Before the development of insulin, diabetics used a substance known as Atlantic starch as a form of diabetic sugar. This is a complex carbohydrate known as inulin, not to be confused with the protein insulin, and was isolated from dahlia tubers. In its native Mexico, the dahlia is simply revered as the National Flower. Meanwhile, in China a new chapter is opening as doctors there use it to treat HIV infections.

Iris And Orris

Irises are widely grown as garden plants and their popularity stems from the wonderful palette of colours seen in their distinctively shaped flowers. The generic name *Iris* is particularly appropriate given that every colour and hue, except for red, can be found in the flowers: in Greek mythology Iris was the messenger of the Gods and the personification of the rainbow. The 17th century Jesuit priest Rene Rapin described this most eloquently when he wrote:

Fair Iris now an endless Pomp supplies,
Which from the radiant Bow that paints the skies,
Draws her proud Name and boasts as many Dyes,
For she her Colour varies and her kind
As ev'ry Season to her Growth's inclin'd.

In the language of flowers, the gift of irises reflected the messenger role of the goddess Iris and signified that the giver had a message for the recipient. Another of Iris's duties was to lead the souls of women to the Elysian Fields and today Greeks often put irises on the graves of women.

Readers with an interest in art will be familiar with the wonderful

Impressionist paintings of irises by Van Gogh and Monet. However, the first paintings of them are at least 3,000 years older and appear on the walls of the great Minoan palace at Knossos. The artist painted a representation of the priest-king and surrounded the figure with many irises. About the same time irises were sculpted in stone on the great wall of the temple of Anon at Karnak in Egypt. Supposedly, Thutmosis III (1504–1450 BCE) had brought them back from his conquest of Asia Minor and begun cultivating them in his garden. There are flowers on the brow of the Sphinx that supposedly are irises. If they are then Thutmosis did not bring irises to Egypt for the Sphinx is 5,000–7,000 years old.

Irises in the form of the 'fleur-de-lis' have been associated with French royalty. The name 'fleur-de-lis' is a corruption of 'fleur-de-Louis', the latter arising because Louis VII adopted it as his emblem for his unsuccessful crusade in 1147. The three parts of the fleur-de-lis are supposed to represent faith, wisdom and valour. Another explanation for the adoption of the fleur-de-lis by the French monarchy dates back to 496 CE when Clovis I was challenging the Germanic army of Alamanni. Clovis found himself trapped between a river and the Germans and needed to escape. Spotting yellow irises growing in the river he realized that the water must be shallow and he led his army safely across. Since the iris had been his salvation, Clovis replaced the three toads on his banner with the tripartite flower. Regardless of how the fleur-de-lis came to represent the French monarchy it became a hated symbol during the Revolution of 1789. It was chipped off buildings and torn from draperies and anyone wearing one was sent to the guillotine. Nevertheless, the iris lives on as a royal symbol: *Iris nigricans*, the black iris of Amman, is the symbol of the Jordanian kings.

Irises were well known to the ancient Greeks and Romans for both used the rhizomes for medicinal purposes. The best rhizomes come from *Iris germanica*, *I. florentina* and *I. pallida* and are known as Orris root. The rhisotomi (root diggers) were the druggists of ancient Greece and according to Pliny the Elder, a 1st century Roman, the best roots came from Illyricum (modern Dalmatia). These probably were from *I. germanica* that grows wild there. Pliny also stated that iris should be gathered only by those in a state of chastity. For medicinal purposes the rhizomes were crushed with wine and used principally as a strong purge for the treatment of dropsy. Orris root powder also was supposed to have magical properties: a small amount applied to the fingernails and touched to the person of one's affection would secure their love. If necessary, the power of the Orris root powder could be enhanced by mixing it with cinnamon.

Apart from being used as an ingredient in many brands of gin, most famously Bombay Sapphire, the principal use of Orris root today is in perfumery. In 19th century Italy, the cultivation of dried iris rhizomes for this purpose was a major industry and the finest Orris root still comes from the region round Florence. After the rhizomes are harvested they are stored for 3–5 years before the Oil of Orris, or Orris Butter, is extracted by steam distillation. The scented component of Orris Butter that is desired by perfumers is a compound known as irone. This has a violet-like odour but is not identical with that of oil of violets. Irone was isolated by the eminent chemist Tiemann who later synthesized a related compound, ionone, which has a scent that much more closely resembles that of violets. The discovery of ionone, which costs about one-eighth of natural oil of violets, popularized violet perfumes and is used widely in cheap perfumes. Quality perfumes contain genuine oil of Orris: not only does it enhance the odour of other fragrant ingredients but it acts as a fixative making the scent last longer after application. One problem with Orris root is that many people are hyper-allergenic to it and it should be absent from any product that claims to be hypo-allergenic.

The use of Orris root as a perfume is nothing new. It was used as a perfume for linen and in 1480 is mentioned in the wardrobe accounts of Edward IV. Around that time, Orris root was put nto water used to wash clothes to give them a pleasant smell in the general absence of soap. This practice is the origin of the term 'swete clothe' that was popular in Elizabethan times. Later, when it became fashionable for ladies to have hair that towered 2 feet above their heads, Orris root was mixed with the starch or flour that was used as the fixative. To think that we complain about the punk fashions of today!

Daffodils, Jonquils And Narcissi

As Winter gives way to Spring the colour yellow makes its way into our consciousness. At head height we find the Cornelian cherry (*Cornus mas*) and the ubiquitous and often garish *Forsythia* whilst at ground level we find swathes of the elegant daffodil in its infinite variety. When the daffodils start to bloom we know that summer is on its way even though winter may still be with us. Not surprisingly, daffodils have been a favourite subject of poets. Everyone is familiar with the vision of Wordsworth's 'host of golden daffodils' but the following quotations tell us more about the Spring climate.

Daffy-down-dilly came up in the cold,
Through the brown mould
Although the March breeze blew keen on her face,
Although the white snow lay in many a place.

Amy Lothrop, *Daffy-Down-Dilly*

It is daffodil time so the robins all cry,
For the sun's a big daffodil up in the sky,
And when down the midnight the owl call 'to-whoo'!
Why, then the round moon is a daffodil too;
Now sheer to the bough-tops the sap starts to climb,
So, merry my masters, it's daffodil time.

Clinton Scollard, *Daffodil Time*

Many people think that daffodils are different from narcissi. A popular misconception is that daffodils carry a single large flower on each stem whereas narcissi stems bear multiple but smaller flowers. In reality, 'daffodil' is the common name for the plants that botanists call *Narcissus*. So, all daffodils are narcissi. Jonquils also are narcissi and their botanical name is *Narcissus jonquilla*. The name 'jonquil' comes from the Spanish *jonquillo* meaning a 'rush' and refers to the semi-cylindrical leaves of certain varieties.

The Swedish pastor, Carl Linnaeus, who gave many of our plants their botanical (Latin) names (chapter 1) clearly was familiar with Greek mythology when he chose the name 'Narcissus' for daffodils. According to legend, Echo was a nymph who was smitten with the youth Narcissus. The gods had bestowed Narcissus with great beauty but in order to keep his good looks he was not allowed to look at his reflection. When Echo's advances were spurned by Narcissus she pined away but not before seeking the help of Nemesis, the goddess of retribution. Nemesis led Narcissus to a shimmering lake where he fell in love with his reflection. Unable to move he faded away. The gods thinking that Nemesis had been too harsh turned him into the flower we know as the narcissus.

Despite the fact that the blooming of daffodils heralds the start of a new growing season, the plants have an association with death. According to one legend, Persephone was wreathed in white daffodils when she was captured by Hades, god of the underworld. Ever since, Greeks and Egyptians have planted daffodils on graves and used wreaths of them at funerals. According to Homer, daffodils grew on the banks of the Acheron, the river of woe, and delighted the spirits of the dead who called them 'asphodel'. The word 'daffodil' is derived from the Dutch *de affodil* (the asphodel) but today the word 'asphodel' refers to a totally different plant that belongs to the lily family.

Daffodils are native to Southern Europe and North Africa and are believed to have been brought to Britain by the Romans. They used the juice from them as a dressing for wounds. This dressing was made by mashing the bulbs into a paste with sufficient starch to glue a wound closed. Given that the juice of daffodils is rich in calcium oxalate it more likely would have irritated the skin than healed the wound. Cut stems of daffodils also release calcium oxalate and this is why daffodils in a mixed bunch will make other flowers wilt. Daffodil juice mixed with honey was used by the Romans to treat sunburn and by the Arabs as a cure for baldness. Roman soldiers are supposed to have carried daffodil bulbs with them to eat should they be seriously wounded in battle. The bulbs contain a series of toxic alkaloids and if one could stomach the bitter taste then death would be swift – but not necessarily painless!

Daffodils may not have been native to Britain but they now are very popular with both gardeners and the horticultural trade. There are somewhere between 25 and 60 species, of which some such as *Narcissus odorus* are natural hybrids, but over 25,000 named varieties! Of these, only about 1,000 are available commercially and only about 300 extensively cultivated. The growth of daffodils for the cut flower trade is focussed on Holland and Britain. In Holland, five varieties account for more than half of the commercial trade and in Britain about 20 varieties. In Britain, this commercial cultivation is largely confined to Lincolnshire, East Anglia, Cornwall, the Channel Islands and the Isles of Scilly. The latter belong to the Duchy of Cornwall and each year Prince Charles is paid one daffodil as rent for unattended lands. One wonders what he does with it.

The miniature daffodil *Narcissus tazetta* is believed to be the oldest daffodil in cultivation as it was known to the ancient Greeks and to the Jews in the Holy Land before the birth of Christ. Because its flowers droop mournfully it was long thought to be an omen of death. Another Mediterranean species that shared a sacred status with *N. tazetta* is the scented *N. triandrus* (Angel Tears). Another scented daffodil from the same region is *N. odorus*. This is a natural hybrid of *N. jonquilla* (the Wild Jonquil) and *N. pseudonarcissus* (the Lent Lily) and is sometimes known as the Campernelle Jonquil or *Narcissus* 'Rugulosus'.

The daffodil is the national flower of Wales and there are two that are unique to the Principality: the Tenby and Welsh daffodils. The origins of the Tenby daffodil (*N. obvallaris*) are obscure. It once was common in the fields around the town of Tenby in South Wales but its popularity in Victorian times resulted in the bulbs being dug up and shipped to Covent Garden market for sale. It has declined even more as the result of property development on land where it once thrived. The Welsh variety is more widespread but just as rare and the easiest place to find them now is in old churchyards since the Victorians planted them around graves.

One of the most attractive daffodils is the scented one known as the Poet's Daffodil (*N. poeticus*). This species, which is naturalized in southern Europe, has a striking white perianth and a small yellow cup with an orange edge and green centre. There also is a double variety (*N. poeticus* 'Plenum') of unknown origin that has been gardened in England since the beginning of the 17th century. Supposedly, Linnaeus gave this variety the name '*poeticus*' because it was so beautiful and was a perfect representation of the poet's story of Narcissus. One named variety of *N. poeticus* is 'Milan'. Presumably it got this name because the city was host to a school of painters who were inspired by Leonardo da Vinci for whom Narcissus was a recurring figure.

One of the best collections of daffodils in the world also is the least known and is to be found at Stourton House Gardens in Wiltshire. The collection was started over 45 years ago and the owner has no idea how many varieties she has as so many have cross-bred and new ones come up each year. Of those varieties that have been registered the one that stands out is 'John Copeland'. This has an incredible scent to go with its intricately entwined petals of yellow and white and at night you can smell it from a long way off. Narcissus would have loved it.

Paeonies: From Panacea To Popular Plant

Like many plant names, the word peony has its origins in Greek mythology. Paeon (or Paion) was the physician of the Olympian gods who reputedly was the first to use the plant's healing powers. According to Homer, Paeon healed Ares and Hades (or Pluto) after Heracles wounded them in the Trojan War. Another Greek healer, Asklepios, was jealous of Paeon and devised a plot to kill him. Hades learned of this plot and in gratitude for being healed turned Paeon into the flower that bears his name.

An alternative legend says that Paeonia was a beautiful nymph who flirted with Apollo. One day they were caught misbehaving by Aphrodite whereupon Paeonia blushed bright red with embarrassment. When the angry Aphrodite turned Paeonia into a flower her blushes became the rose-coloured flowers. This legend appears in a poem written in 1665 by the French Jesuit priest Rene Rapin:

Erect in all her scarlet Pomp you'll see
With busy leaves the graceful Peony;
Whose blushes might the Praise of Virtue claim,
But her vile Scent betrays they rise from Shame.

In China the peony is known as the Queen of Flowers and it is called 'Sho

Yo' meaning 'most beautiful'. It is the flower of riches and honour, symbolises wealth and distinction and it is an omen of good fortune. Paintings of peonies often are hung in Chinese homes to bring good luck and in offices to bring good business. In the ancient Chinese Shi Jing (Book of Odes), amorous youths and maidens gave each other peonies as a symbol of love and affection. Peonies also are one of the main motifs of Chinese decorative arts and can be found on porcelain, in woodblock and screen paintings, and embroidered onto tapestries and clothing. The significance of peonies to the Chinese is emphasized by the use of subtle lines in paintings of them to depict their life force.

Peonies were introduced to Japan some time between the 8th and 11th centuries. Like the Chinese, the Japanese incorporated images of the plant into their paintings, porcelain and tapestries and descriptions of it feature in many poems and other forms of literature. In the West, by contrast, the peony does not feature much in literature and art and Shakespeare only makes a passing reference to it in act 4 of *The Tempest.*

Given the role of Paeon in Greek mythology, it is likely that the first use of peonies was for medicinal purposes. Early texts on Chinese medicine describe 3 peony preparations for treating blood disorders and for staunching the flow of blood from wounds. In the First Century CE, Pliny the Elder described 20 different illnesses that were cured by various parts of the plant. Later, Dioscorides described male and female peonies but these were misnomers for the so-called 'female' was *P. officinalis* and the 'male' was *P. mascula*. In the Middle Ages these plants were used to treat childbirth, teething pain, bad dreams, jaundice, epileptic seizures and gall stones as well as warding off evil spirits. Put simply, they were considered a panacea. John Keats, the poet, described their use in treating melancholy:

But when the melancholy fit shall fall
Sudden from heaven, like a weeping cloud
That fosters the droop-headed flowers all,
And hides the green hill in an April shroud;
Then glut thy sorrow on a morning rose
Or on the wealth of globed peonies.

The cultivation of peonies as ornamental plants, rather than for medicinal purposes, began in China during the 7th century. During the T'ang dynasty from 618–906 CE peonies became very popular in the imperial gardens. During the Sung dynasty, which began at the end of the 10th century, peonies had spread throughout China. The Sung capital of Louyang became a centre for peony culture, a distinction that it retains today. Much later, the city of HeZe (formerly Caozhou) became the second centre for peony culture.

There are two types of peony that occur in the wild: herbaceous peonies and tree peonies. The foliage of herbaceous peonies dies back to the ground each winter and in spring new shoots emerge from the soil. Despite their name, tree peonies are really small shrubs. Each winter they lose their leaves but a woody stem remains. Both types are found in China and once they became popular with the emperors horticulturists began breeding new double-flowered forms. It is believed that they began grafting valued cultivars as early as the 12th century. At the same time, Japanese breeders began simplifying the flowers. Today, most Japanese herbaceous peonies have a rounded centre made of small petals with wider petals surrounding the centre. This is known as the Japanese form.

Tree peonies are not indigenous to Europe but herbaceous peonies are. One indigenous species is *P. officinalis* that is found widely between France and Albania. When it came to England is not known but the celebrated Abbot of Eynsham, Aelfric, recorded its presence in 995 CE. The so-called male peony, *P. mascula*, was introduced by Augustinian monks when they settled on the island of Steep Holm in the Bristol Channel in the 12th century. Another important species is *P. lactiflora* but this did not arrive in England until 1808 when nurseryman Reginald Whitley sourced it from Canton. The breeding of new varieties of peony in Europe began in France in the latter half of the 19th century. One famous breeder was Victor Lemoine although he is better known for his lilacs.

In England, James Kelway began breeding peonies at his nursery in Langport in Somerset. Although *P. lactiflora* has unspectacular single pink flowers, Kelway recognized its breeding potential. His breakthrough came when he crossed it with the red-flowered *P. mascula*. He had discovered the latter on a day trip to Steep Holm where it had survived the collapse of the

Augustinian monastery. The early hybrids were shorter plants and many had exotic flowers that greatly appealed to Victorian gardeners. Many of these were named after famous people of the time including painters (e.g. Augustus John), composers (e.g. Sir Edward Elgar) and politicians (e.g. Lord Kitchener). Sometimes a peony variety changed its name from one person to another, perhaps because the celebrity fell from favour. With the peony no longer selling well it would be renamed after somebody more in vogue.

One of the original features of Kelway's nursery was Peony Valley, a 10 acre field that sloped on each side and contained a representative selection of the best varieties of peonies. The Great Western railway line ran across the bottom of the field and in the heyday of the nursery a temporary railway halt, Peony Valley Halt, was opened each June. Trains would make special stops there and passengers could stroll through the lines of flowers.

The tree peony, *P. suffruiticosa*, did not make an appearance in Europe until 1787 when Dr John Duncan of the East India Company presented one to Sir Joseph Banks at Kew Gardens. This did not survive long and it was followed by a consignment of a further seven plants in 1794. Obtaining subsequent plants from China proved very difficult and it was not until the 186's that stocks became available from nurseries. In the 1880s tree peonies became available from Japan and these were more popular than the Chinese varieties because they had a lighter blooming habit. About this time there was major breakthrough in the breeding of tree peonies when Victor Lemoine crossed *P. suffruiticosa* with *P.lutea* and created the first yellow hybrid tree peony. This is known as *Paeonia x lemoinei* 'Alice Harding'.

Tree peonies and herbaceous peonies have different flowering periods and botanists do not consider them to be closely related. Consequently, it was believed that the two groups could not be crossed. However, in 1948 a Japanese nurseryman called Toichi Itoh succeeded in crossing the tree peony 'Alice Harding' with the herbaceous *P. lactiflora* 'Kakoden'. Nine of the original 36 seedlings that he generated had the foliage of tree peonies but the growth habit of herbaceous peonies in that they die back to the ground each winter. These plants are known as Itoh hybrids or inter-sectional hybrids. The development of these plants has increased the range of colours available for herbaceous peonies and introduced the flares that are characteristic of tree peonies.

What Is A Marigold?

The common name 'marigold' is used to describe a number of different plants: African marigolds (*Tagetes erecta*), French marigolds (*Tagetes patula*), Mexican mint marigold (*Tagetes lucida*), pot marigolds (*Calendula officinalis*), Cape marigolds (*Dimorphotheca sp.*) and marsh marigolds (*Caltha palustris*). All of them are members of the daisy family (Asteraceae) except for the marsh marigold that belongs to the buttercup family (Ranunculaceae). If the confusion created by the use of the term 'marigold' was not enough to convince you of the benefits of using the Latin binomial system introduced by Linnaeus (chapter 1), consider the Mexican mint marigold. Its other common names are Spanish or winter tarragon but another member of the daisy family, *Artemisia dracunculus sativa*, is the source of the herb we usually call French tarragon or simply tarragon.

The name 'marigold' is a corruption of 'Mary's gold'. This description refers in part to the colour of the flowers and partly to their association with the Virgin Mary. Early monks and nuns believed that the Virgin Mary wore a marigold on her bosom as a material symbol of the golden glow radiating around her head. An alternative explanation is that marigolds of the genus *Calendula* could be induced to flower almost every month of the year in monastery and ecclesiastical gardens. Thus they were always in bloom for any feast associated with the Virgin Mary and could be used for decorating churches. The name *Calendula* is derived from the Latin 'kalendae', meaning first day of the month, presumably because they are in bloom at the start of most months.

Another explanation for the name 'marigold' is that it is derived from the Saxon name 'ymbglidegold' which means 'it turns with the sun'. This is a reference to the observation that the flowers of many members of the daisy family move so that they always are directly facing the sun. In the early seventeenth century, the poet George Wither described the marigold always facing the sun, personified by Phoebus, when he wrote:

When with serious musing I behold
The grateful and obsequious Marigold
How duly every morning she displays
Her open breast when Phoebus spreads his rays;
How she observes him in his daily walk,
Still bending toward him her small slender stalk;
How, when he down declines, she droops and mourns,
Bedewed, as t'were, with tears till he returns;
And how she veils her flowers when he is gone,
As if she scorn'd to be looked upon
By an inferior eye, or did contemn
To wait upon a meaner light than him.

The latter part of this verse refers to another feature of calendulas: they close up their flowers when the sun goes down. Other writers of this time who commented on this include Shakespeare and the horticulturist Thomas Hyll.

The specific epithet '*officinalis*' in the name *Calendula officinalis* indicates that the plant has medicinal properties. The plant is a native of the Mediterranean region and it is known that it was used in ancient Greek, Roman and Arabic cultures for the treatment of various ailments. In the 12th century Macer claimed that merely looking at the plant would improve the eyesight, clear the head and encourage cheerfulness. How I wish! Interest in *Calendula* continues to this day and herbalists recommend it for the treatment of various skin disorders including bruising, burns and scalds, acne, impetigo, chilblains, nappy rash, skin ulcers and other slow-healing wounds.

Cosmetically it is used to treat minor skin damage such as sub-dermal broken capillaries and sunburn. *Calendula* extracts, if taken internally, can relieve the symptoms associated with gastric and duodenal ulcers.

The common name for *C. officinalis*, pot marigold, is a reference to its use in cooking as a cheap substitute for saffron, a practice that began with the Romans. It still is used as a food colorant today, particularly in poultry feed where it imparts egg yolks with a deep yellow colour. It also has been used as a dye for fabrics and cosmetics. In the latter case, the 16th century herbalist William Turner complained 'Some use it to make their heyre yellow with the floure of this herbe, not beying content with the naturall colour which God hath geven them.'

Linnaeus gave the name *Tagetes* to African and French marigolds in honour of Tages, the grandson of Jupiter. According to legend, Tages sprung out of a ploughed field and began teaching the Etruscans the (very) obscure art of haruspicy. This is the practice of foretelling lightning, winds, eclipses and the like from examining entrails (a fact that I am sure you knew already!). How Linnaeus made this link is open to question.

The African marigold, *Tagetes erecta*, was discovered in Tunis in 1535 by troops of Emperor Charles v. He had gone there to help free 22,000 Christian slaves held captive by the Moors. When the flower reached England it was assumed to be a native of North Africa and was given the name Flos Africanus. Over 200 years later it was discovered to be a native of Mexico. It is assumed that it had travelled back to Spain with the conquistadors and then somehow made its way to North Africa. The French marigold, *T. patula*, also is found in North Africa but originated in Mexico. It is believed to have come to Britain with Huguenot refugees fleeing France after the Massacre of St Bartholomew in 1572. In their native Mexico, *Tagetes sp.* are known as the flower of the dead since they supposedly sprang from the blood of the native Indians slaughtered by the conquistadors.

After its arrival in Europe, *Tagetes* was transported to India and quickly became important in the rites and rituals of everyday life. They are used as offerings and decoration for places of worship, at funerals, weddings and other ceremonies. During the festival of Holi people splash each other with coloured water. Marigolds are popular at this time because a yellow liquid is produced if they are left soaking after being boiled in water. Floriculture, the commercial cultivation of flowers, is big business in India and marigolds are one of the most popular plants, especially for garlands. Part of this popularity can be explained by their widespread religious use. More important, they are easy to cultivate and are robust enough not to require expensive packaging or processing.

In Western cultures, *Tagetes* and *Calendula* are not used much as cut flowers; rather, they are used mostly as bedding plants. Perhaps they should be used more widely for they are effective for pest control. If *Calendula* is used as a companion plant with tomatoes it will keep the latter free of insect pests. Some varieties of *Tagetes* have an unpleasant fragrance and those that do repel a wide variety of insects as well as rabbits. In addition, the roots of *Tagetes* excrete a substance that kills nematode worms. With the growing popularity of organic vegetables perhaps marigolds will become as popular in Europe as they are in India.

Carnations, Coups And Contented Cows

The genus *Dianthus* has many species and includes such garden favourites as carnations, pinks and sweet Williams. The wild carnation or clove pink (*D. caryophyllus*) is a native of the Mediterranean and was first called *diosanthus*, or divine flower, by the Greek philosopher Theophrastus (370-285 BCE). Over time the plant acquired many different names and it appears in literature as 'gilofre' (Chaucer), 'gillyvore' (Shakespeare), 'gillyflower' and 'gilloflower'. All these common names are believed to be derived from the Arabic word for clove, *quaranful*. This is a reference to the aromatic smell of the leaves and provides an explanation for the specific epithet *caryophillus* (*caryon*, nut; *phyllus*, leaf) and the name of the family (Caryophyllaceae) to which *Dianthus* belongs. Another common name was 'Sops in Wine' and this derives from the practice of dunking the plant in wine and ale to impart a clove-like flavour to it.

The origin of the word 'carnation' is not clear. Some scholars think that the word is derived from the Greek *corone*, meaning flower garlands, as it was one of the flowers used in Greek ceremonial crowns. Others believe that it is derived from the Latin *carnis*, meaning flesh, a reference to the original colour of the flower. Alternatively, it is derived from *incarnacyon* meaning the incarnation of God made flesh. This latter explanation fits with the observation that carnations often appear in paintings of the Virgin Mary and baby Jesus. Good examples are Raphael's Madonna of the Pinks and Durer's Madonna of the Carnation. Some people think that the name 'pink' is derived from the frilled edge of the flowers that look as if they have been cut with pinking scissors. However, the name 'pink' was in use long before 1893 when pinking scissors were invented and in fact they got their name from the flower.

The name 'Sweet William' refers specifically to *Dianthus barbatus*, the specific epithet *barbatus* meaning bearded. The origin of its common name is unclear. One explanation is that it is derived from the French *oeillet*, meaning little eye, and that this got corrupted to 'Willy' and then 'William'. Another is that it is derived from Saint William whose festival is on 25 June when the flower is in bloom. Yet another explanation is that it is named after William the Conqueror or William Shakespeare. Regardless of how Sweet William got its name it is often used in English ballads to describe a lovelorn young man – and a perfect partner for a wallflower!

The wild carnation or clove pink (*D. caryophillus*) and the wild pink (*D. plumarius*) are believed to have come to England with William the Conqueror. He imported stone from Caen in France to build some of his castles and this carried seeds of both of these pinks as well as those of the wallflower (*Erysimum cheiri*). Initially the wild pink struggled to survive but it had established itself by the middle of the 16th century. Both pinks have gone wild in the south of England and often can be seen growing on the walls of Norman castles. Sweet William (*D. barbatus*) arrived somewhat later, about 1573. Just over 100 years later, in 1691, a London nurseryman called Thomas Fairchild made history by creating the first recorded artificial hybrid. He crossed *D. caryophillus* with *D. barbatus* to form a variety known as 'Fairchild's Mule' and a specimen is preserved in the Natural History Museum in London. Fairchild has another claim to fame. He founded the Society of Gardeners, an association of growers who discussed their latest plant finds and new nursery techniques. In 1730 they published the Catalogus Plantatum, a comprehensive catalogue of all available plant material in England, pre-dating the Royal Horticultural Society's Plant Finder by over 250 years!

Since the original breeding experiment of Fairchild hundreds of different varieties of *Dianthus* have been produced, some by crossing different plants and others from propagation of occasional sports. The most famous undoubtedly are the powerfully-scented Malmaisons whose name derives from the fact that the first one resembled a new rose called 'Souvenir de la Malmaison'. The first Malmaison carnation, known as 'Old Blush', arose in France and came to England in the early 1860s. By 1876 it had produced three sports: 'Lady Middleton', 'Souvenir de la Malmaison Crimson' and 'Princess of Wales'. Shortly thereafter there were many more, each with very distinctive floral colours and patterns. Unfortunately, Malmaison carnations are not easy to grow. A combination of most estate gardeners going off to fight in the First World War and a virus affecting the plants meant that they nearly died out. Fortunately, they had survived in two Scottish gardens and in recent years National Plant Collection holder Jim Marshall has been building up stocks by micropropagation.

Two other names associated with carnations deserve a mention. One of the most famous varieties is Mrs Sinkins. John Thomas Sinkins was the Master of the Slough Workhouse in the mid-1870s and a keen grower of pinks. Among his collection he found a heavily-perfumed double-fringed white variety. He sold his stock to Charles Turner, owner of the Royal Nurseries in Slough, on condition that he named it after his wife. Slough has capitalised on the fame of *Dianthus* 'Mrs Sinkins': the town coat of arms consists of a swan, representing the River Thames, holding the flower in its beak. At the beginning of the 20th century, Sussex nurseryman Montague Allwood tried to improve the short flowering season of pinks and eventually achieved success by crossing cottage and clove pinks to produce repeat-flowering border pinks (*Dianthus x allwoodii*).

The world of carnations is rife with symbolism. The Elizabethans believed that anyone wearing a carnation would never die on the scaffold. This may have led to the popularity of carnations as buttonholes. If an engaged girl wore a carnation it signalled to her suitors that they may as well give up hope. The flowers were symbolic of marital bliss and fecundity. At his wedding ceremony, Maximilian of Austria was instructed by the Bishop of Treves to search under his bride's wedding dress for a carnation hidden there. This he did, first tentatively and then with increasing enthusiasm. In some parts of the United States and Canada, carnations are worn on Mother's Day: a red carnation signifies that one's mother is still alive and a white one that she is dead. At Oxford University, tradition decrees that students should wear a white carnation for their first exam, a red one for their last exam and a pink one for all exams in between. The origin of this custom is unknown but clearly it finds favour with the local florists. Oscar Wilde often wore a green carnation. When asked what it signified, he replied 'Nothing whatever, but that is just what nobody will guess'. Later, Noel Coward in his 1929 musical *Bittersweet* publicised green carnations as a symbol of homosexuality with the lyrics:

Pretty boys, witty boys,
You may sneer
At our disintegration.
Haughty boys, naughty boys,
Dear, dear, dear.
Swooning with affectation...
And as we are the reason
For the Nineties being gay,
We all wear a green carnation.

In Portugal, carnations are symbolic of the almost bloodless, leftist, military-led coup of 1974 that effectively changed the country from an authoritarian dictatorship to a liberal democracy. The dictatorship started in 1926 and for most of its life was led by Oliveira Salazar. He was replaced in 1968 by Marcelo Caetano who quickly fell out with General Antonio Spinola over the promotion of military officers and Portuguese colonial policy. Supporters of Spinola staged a coup on 25 April 1974 and the government of Caetano quickly capitulated. Despite radio appeals for the population to stay at home, Portuguese descended on the streets and mixed with the military insurgents. Being April, the flower markets were full of carnations and civilians took to placing these in the barrels of the soldier's guns. An image of such an event was flashed around the world on television and gave rise to the name 'Carnation Revolution'.

The name 'Carnation' has an unlikely association with condensed milk. In 1899, grocer E.A. Stuart founded the Pacific Coast Condensed Milk Company in Washington State in the US. As sales began to grow, Stuart searched for the perfect name for his product. Walking in downtown Seattle he passed a tobacconist's window displaying cigars called 'Carnation'. He thought it an absurd name for a cigar but perfect for his condensed milk that thereafter became Carnation milk. Later he established his own farm, Carnation farm, where he kept pedigree cows to produce the raw milk. Ever a marketer, he coined the phrase 'Carnation Condensed Milk, the milk from Contented Cows™'. Carnation Farm was located in Tolt and in 1917 the township changed its name to Carnation. This name change did not sit well with the Indians and local pioneers. In 1928 the name changed back to Tolt but, just to confuse things, the railroad station and post office were still known as Carnation. Given the uncertainty surrounding the plant name this confusion could be considered appropriate.

A Profusion Of Lilies

The word 'lily' appears in the name of many plants: water lily, day lily, arum lily, calla lily, Easter lily, Lent lily, Madonna lily, Jersey lily, giant lily, tiger lily, lily of the valley and plain old lily. Quite a few of these plants do not even belong to the lily family (Liliaceae)! To further add to the confusion, some of the common names apply to more than one plant. Thus the name 'tiger lily' has been applied to a day lily, *Hemerocallis fulva*, and 4 different *Lilium* species: *L. columbianum*, *L. lancifolium*, *L.philadelphicum* and *L.michiganense*. Similarly, most people consider *Lilium longiflorum* to be the Easter lily but to Irish Republicans it is *Zantedeschia aethiopica*. Here we shall confine our discussion to the true lilies, i.e. species of *Lilium*.

According to Greek mythology, the Madonna lily (*L. candidum*) and the galaxy known as the Milky Way had a common origin. Zeus, who was king of the gods, wanted his illegitimate infant son Heracles to be made a god. His wife Hera, stepmother of Heracles, objected strongly. Consequently, Zeus ordered Somnus, the god of sleep, to give Hera a potion to make her sleep. Whilst she was asleep, Zeus put Heracles to Hera's breast so that Heracles would drink her milk and become immortal. Heracles drank greedily and so much milk flowed that some splashed across the heavens where it formed the Milky Way. A few drops fell to earth and became the pure white flower we know as the Madonna lily. A magnificent painting by the artist Tintoretto shows Zeus in the act of putting Heracles to Hera's breast but does not show the formation of lilies.

The Madonna lily is a native of the eastern Mediterranean region and Asia Minor. The earliest records of it are from pottery and jewellery, 3,500 years old, that was unearthed at the archaeological site at Knossos in Crete. Coincidentally, one of the main gods worshipped at Knossos was Zeus. In this early Cretan civilization lilies were moulded onto gold jewellery and this may be the origin of the expression 'gilding the lily'. Another explanation for the term is that it is a corruption from Shakespeare's play *King John*:

> *Therefore, to be posses'd with double pomp,*
> *To guard a title that was rich before,*
> *To gild refined gold, to paint the lily,*
> *To throw a perfume on the violet,*
> *To smooth the ice, or add another hue*
> *Unto the rainbow, or with taper light*
> *To seek the beauteous eye of heaven to garnish,*
> *Is wasteful and ridiculous excess.*

As the words above show, 'gild the lily' does not appear in the original text and is a misquotation.

As with so many things, the Romans adopted the Greek respect for the Madonna lily and associated it with their queen of the gods. They also used it medicinally, turning it into a salve for wounds, an ointment for burns and a cure for corns. With all the marching that legionnaires did it is no surprise that they took bulbs of it everywhere they went! A consequence of this is that the Madonna lily is found in every territory that the Romans conquered and they certainly introduced it to England. The use of a burn salve derived from lilies continued until recent times as did a beauty treatment first described by Dioscorides (41–68 CE). He claimed that when lily bulbs were mashed with honey and applied to the face it would produce clear skin and prevent wrinkles. Nothing changes in the world of cosmetics!

The Venerable Bede (673–735 CE) who worshipped at the monastery at Wearmouth and Jarrow is credited with making the Madonna lily a symbol of the Virgin Mary. The first pictorial representation of the lily is in an illuminated manuscript painted by the monks of Winchester cathedral in the 10th century. From this time on nearly all paintings of the Virgin Mary and the Annunciation include the Madonna lily. Famous examples include the depiction of the Annunciation by the 14th century painter Simone Martini and the 19th century painter Dante Gabriel Rossetti. Once the flower became associated with the Virgin Mary it was seen as representing purity in all its aspects, so much so that in many churches the golden stamens and pistils were removed from the lilies used to decorate the altar.

After the Madonna lily, the next lilies to arrive in England were two Turkscap varieties: *L.chalcedonium* and *L.martagon*. There are records of both in the late 16th century but they may have been introduced much earlier by soldiers returning from the Crusades. Chalcedon is close to present-day Istanbul and near Greece, the natural home of *L.chalcedonia*. A 'martagon' is a kind of turban seen in Turkey hence the name 'Turkscap' for these lilies. The next lilies to be introduced to England came not from Asia Minor but from the Orient and originally were collected by the French priests Pere Armand David and Pere Delavay. William Kerr, after whom the shrub *Kerria* is named, was a plant hunter who was based in China for 8 years. In 1804 he sent back specimens of *L.lancifolium*. In most parts of the world this plant is known as the Tiger lily since its floral markings resemble those of the big cat. However, in North America the name 'Tiger lily' refers to their native *L.philadelphicum*. Another popular lily, *L.longiflorum*, was discovered in the Ryukyu islands of southern Japan in 1777 by Carl Peter Thunberg but did not reach England until 1819. This lily now is a great favourite in the USA and is a popular potted plant at Easter.

The Regal lily (*L.regale*) was discovered in 1904 by one of the great plant hunters of all times, Ernest Wilson. He is credited with introducing over 1,000 new plants to Western gardeners and *L.regale* is considered one of his best finds. In 1910, Wilson made his fourth expedition to China and travelled over 2,000 miles to the area near the border with Tibet where he first found the Regal lily. According to Wilson, when the lily flowered 'a lonely semi-desert region was [transformed] into a veritable fairyland'. On the way back from this expedition Wilson's mule train was caught in an avalanche and he fractured his leg when he was thrown against a rock. Unfortunately, another mule train was coming the other way and the only way it could pass was for Wilson to lie on his back and let more than 40 mules step over him. The fractured leg never healed properly and Wilson was lucky that it did not need to be amputated. However he was left with what he called his 'lily limp'. Having survived a near disaster in China he ended up dying a few years later in a car accident in the United States.

After *L.longiflorum* was introduced to England it was taken to Bermuda by missionaries in 1853. An American lady visiting Bermuda in the 1880s saw the lilies in flower and, entranced by them, took some bulbs back home to Philadelphia. A local nurseryman there began growing them and forcing them into bloom for Easter. Demand for these 'Easter lilies' outstripped supply and soon production switched back to Bermuda. After a virus destroyed the Bermudan crop production moved to Japan, the place from where this lily originated! After the outbreak of World War II, production moved yet again, this time to the California –Oregon border. Today, just 10 farms produce 95 per cent of the bulbs that produce blooms that sell for over $40 million in the two week period around Easter. Almost all of these plants are a variety known as 'Nellie White', selected by lily grower James White on account of its exceptionally large, pure white trumpets. The spiritual essence of the Easter lily is captured in the words of Louise Lewin Matthews:

Easter morn with lilies fair
Fills the church with perfumes rare,
As their clouds of incense rise,
Sweetest offerings to the skies.
Stately lilies pure and white
Flooding darkness with their light,
Bloom and sorrow drift away,
On this holy hallow'd day.
Easter lilies bending low
In the golden afterglow,
Bear a message from the sod
To the heavenly towers of God.

One of the people who worked on the farms producing Easter lilies was Leslie Woodriff. He was a keen breeder of begonias and lilies and eventually set himself up as an independent grower. One day he observed an oriental lily with an up-facing bloom that opened to give a vivid pink flower with a white border. He gave it the name 'Stargazer'. This strongly scented variety now is one of the most popular lilies for the cut-flower market. Although Woodriff now is dead, his name lives on the lily world as two hybrids are named after him: 'Woodriff's Memory' and 'Leslie Woodriff'.

Whilst we in the West grow lilies for their floral beauty, in China they are grown for the luxury and health food market. The bulbs are starchy and *L.lancifolium*, *L.pumilum* and *L.brownii* are grown on a large scale and sold in dry form. Before cooking they are reconstituted and then stir fried or grated and used to thicken soup. Alternatively, they can be baked and when eaten taste like baked potatoes. Lilies are most popular in the summer because of their ability to reduce internal heat. The idea of eating lilies has spread to some up-market restaurants in the US where the chefs add lily flowers to sauces to give them an exotic taste. My taste is to keep the flowers in the garden and out of the kitchen.

Sages, Salvias And Shamans

The word 'sage' can be a source of some confusion as it is used to describe many different plants. When used without modifiers, sage generally refers to the culinary herb whose botanical name is *Salvia officinalis*. Many other *Salvia* species also are known as sages, e.g. *S. divinorum* is the Diviner's sage and *S. argentea* is silver sage. Two closely related genera also are known as sages: *Perovskia atriplicifolia* is known as Russian sage and the common name of *Phlomis fruticosa* is Jerusalem sage. Sages are members of the family Lamiaceae and should not be confused with the sagebrush (*Artemisia tridentata*) familiar to aficionados of Western movies and a member of the daisy family.

A feature of the sages is that they have a very characteristic aroma. However the flowers are not scented. Rather, the epidermal glands on the leaves emit fragrant oils with an aromatic scent familiar to anyone who has been to the Mediterranean region in the height of summer. Sages produce these oils for a number of reasons: to protect the plant from the heat of the sun and to keep away browsing animals. Gardeners can make use of the latter feature and plant sage alongside cabbages and carrots to deter cabbage moths, carrot fly, beetles and slugs. However, sage is not compatible with all plants. In the garden it will inhibit the growth of cucumbers, probably for the same reason that chaparral sage (*S. leucophylla*) inhibits nearby grasses.

The sage species used as herbs are native to the Mediterranean and Asia Minor and flourish on limestone where there is very little soil. The best quality sage comes from the islands of Veglia and Cherso near Fiume in Croatia where the surrounding district is known as the sage region. The value of sage was known to the ancient Greeks and to the Romans who used it for both culinary and medicinal purposes. The healing powers of sage are reflected in its botanical name: *Salvia* is derived from the Latin 'salveo' which means 'to heal'. So important was sage to the ancient Romans that they followed an elaborate ceremony when harvesting it. A sage gatherer would wear clean clothes and have clean feet and would use a special non-iron knife as iron reacts with chemicals in the sage.

The common sage (*S.officinalis*) and its close relatives are credited with many beneficial effects. Chewing the leaves will whiten the teeth but an infusion of the leaves will darken hair that is growing grey. A few sprigs of sage in the bath will provide relief for aching muscles and this probably would have found favour with the Romans. A tea made from the leaves will reduce sweating when drunk cold and this was used to provide TB patients with relief from night sweats. However, if the tea is drunk hot it will induce sweating. Infusions of the leaves also were used to promote healing of wounds, as a cure for heartburn, as a gargle for sore throats, to reduce the side effects of the menopause and to facilitate conception. All these benefits led to the saying, ascribed to Martin Luther, 'Why should a man die whilst sage grows in his garden'? The response from Hildegard of Bingen was '...because nothing can stand against death'. The belief in the medicinal benefits of sage was not confined to Europeans. At the height of the tea trade with China, English and Dutch merchants exchanged one crate of sage for three crates of tea.

Sage is widely used as a culinary herb in Western cooking, particularly in English, French, German and Italian dishes that are based on poultry or pork. Apart from its characteristic taste, sage counteracts the effects of fat in meat. Sage also can be added to bread, pizza dough, pasta sauces and soups made from pulses. It has long been used to improve the flavour of cheese as John Gay (1685–1732) noted in *The Shepherd's Week*:

'*Marbled with Sage, the hardening cheese she pressed.*'

The cheese in question probably was Derby cheese for this has been flavoured with sage from at least the 17th century.

Not everything about sage is good news. First, it is considered bad luck to plant sage in your own garden so a stranger should be found to do it for you. Second, a full bed of sage brings ill health so another plant should share the garden plot. Finally, there is an old saying that expresses the sexual connotation of sage:

If the sagebush thrives and grows,
The master's not master – and he knows!

This implies that if sage thrives in the garden only girls would be born to the family. Consequently, husbands who did not want to be nagged by a gaggle of women would destroy perfectly healthy sage plants.

Whereas *S. officinalis* was introduced to Britain by the Romans, the biennial Clary (*S. sclarea*) did not arrive until 1562. The specific epithet *sclarea* is derived from the Latin *claurus* for clear or bright and reflects a medicinal use of the seeds. When soaked in water the seeds form sticky mucilage that was used for bathing and soothing the eyes and for removing particulates. This mucilage also is effective in facilitating the removal of thorns and splinters. In Germany, the flowers of Clary and elder were added to Rhine wine to make it taste like a good Muscatel and hence the plant is sometimes referred to as Muscatel sage. The leaves also have been used as a substitute for hops and this practice supposedly generates a more intoxicating brew. According to one writer: 'Some brewers of Ale and Beere doe put it into their drinke to make it more heady, fit to please drunkards, who thereby, according to their several dispositions, become either dead drunke, or foolish drunke, or madde drunke.' Nothing new there!

The oil produced by *S. sclarea* is known as Clary oil and is mainly used as a fixer in the perfume industry. Fixers form the base notes of perfumes and their function is to make the fragrance last longer on the skin. The waxy mass left behind after solvent extraction of Clary leaves is known as a *concrete* and this is mixed with other scented plant materials such as jasmine and lavender and incorporated into soaps and lotions. Clary oil also is used by aromatherapists for hormone balancing in women and the most important constituent of the oil for this purpose is believed to be a chemical called sclareol. One US company now is breeding Clary varieties with greatly enhanced sclareol content.

Chia (*S. hispanica*) was cultivated for centuries by the Aztecs of Mexico and the native Americans of the South-West United States. They used it as a high energy endurance food, or 'running food'. When the seeds are consumed with water they swell to form thick mucilage composed of complex carbohydrates. This mucilage breaks down slowly in the gut to release sugar over a long period whilst warding off hunger pangs. Thus, provided a supply of water always was available, a small and lightweight bag of seeds was sufficient sustenance for a march of many days.

Diviner's sage (*S. divinorum*) is a plant that differs from all other sages. It occurs in the wild in only one place, the Mazateca region of Mexico, where it was used by the by the local shamans to engender a spiritual or mystical experience. This was possible because the plant synthesizes a psychoactive substance known as salvinorin A that is released when the leaves are chewed, smoked or drunk as a tea. The shamans used it to divine what was wrong with the patient and how to treat them. Ethnobotanists consider Diviner's sage to be an entheogen, a plant that causes God to be within an individual. When administered to the indigenous people by the shamans that undoubtedly was the effect and, as a salvia, it truly would have a healing effect. Unfortunately, the drug community discovered it in the 1960s and use it to go on psychedelic trips: hardly a healing experience!

Napoleon's Flower

Violets are species of *Viola* and the name is derived from Greek mythology. There are many different variations of the legend but the basic story is that Zeus had a lover called Io even though he was married to Hera. When Hera found out about the illicit affair, Zeus turned Io into a white heifer and let her graze in a field of violets. Hera saw the heifer eating the violets and its perfect beauty aroused her suspicions. She asked Zeus to give her the calf and he was trapped into assenting. Hera then wreaked her revenge on Io and harassed her so much that Io plunged into the sea that ever since has borne her name (Ionian Sea). In the 14th century, the Greek dramatist called Athens the violet-crowned city because the name of the king who was crowned there (Ion) and the flower (ion = violet) were the same. The English writer Macaulay used the same term when he wrote of Athens and today the violet is the city emblem.

To the ancient Romans, violets were the symbol of mourning and of affection for the dead. They decorated tombs with wreaths of violets on the Festival of the Dead in February and on the Festival of the Violets at the end of March. In the Middle Ages violets came to symbolise faithfulness in love and in the 19th century Percy Bysse Shelley commemorated the grief of a lost love in his poem *On a Faded Violet*.

The odour from the flower is gone
Which like thy kisses breathed on me;
The colour from the flower is flown
Which glowed on thee and only thee!

A shrivelled, lifeless, vacant form,
It lies on my abandoned breast,
And mocks the heart which yet is warm,
With cold and silent rest.

An infusion made from *Viola tricolor* was supposed to mend a broken heart and so became known as heartsease or love–in–idleness. Shakespeare was familiar with this connotation and in *A Midsummer Night's Dream* Oberon describes how he watched the flight of Cupid's arrow intended for a vestal virgin:

Yet marked I where the bolt of Cupid fell:
It fell upon a little western flower,
Before milk-white, now purple with love's wound,
And maidens call it love-in-idleness.

Oberon commands Puck to fetch this flower because it makes 'Man or woman madly dote/ Upon the next live creature that it sees'. He intends to streak it on the eyes of Queen Titania so that on waking she will dote upon Bottom who has been transformed into an ass.

In Christian art, the violet symbolizes the humility of the Virgin Mary. One legend states that violets were white until Mary was filled with anguish from watching her son, Christ, suffer upon the cross whereupon they turned purple (why purple?). Perhaps this is why purple is a popular colour for the robes of church officials. In Renaissance painting, Mary is often depicted with violets to symbolize her humility. A good example is the work completed around 1430 by the German artist Stephen Lochner that is known as *Madonna of the Violets*. Another painting completed about the same time was *Madonna of Humility* and in it the Italian painter Giovanni Paolo has included tiny violets.

Humility certainly was not a characteristic of Napoleon, the most famous aficionado of violets. His love for them started when he was a boy growing up in Corsica. His wife Josephine had a corsage of violets at their wedding and he gave her a bouquet of violets on every anniversary. Napoleon divorced Josephine in 1809 because she could not bear him any children and his second wife, Marie Louise of Austria turned out (fortunately!) to be a lover of violets. In 1814, Napoleon was forced to abdicate and he was exiled to the island of Elba. Before his departure for Elba he told his friends that, like the violet, he would return in the spring. As a consequence, the Bonapartists took to wearing violet-coloured clothing and nicknamed Napoleon 'Corporal Violet'. In 1815 he did return, only to be defeated at Waterloo and banished to the remote island of St Helena. His first wife Josephine had died whilst he was on Elba and he had violets planted on her grave. Before leaving for his exile on St Helena, Napoleon picked some of these violets and they later were found in a locket that he wore around his neck.

In 1816, after Napoleon was exiled to St Helena, the Austrian government sent Marie Louise to rule the Duchy of Parma, Piacenza and Guastella. What a fortunate posting for Parma was home to a variety of violets that were characterized by double flowers and an exquisite perfume. Napoleon must have been spitting mad by the injustice of it! As soon as she arrived in Parma, Marie Louise took charge of the cultivation of Parma violets in the botanic gardens and at her summer residence in Colorno. She also used the violet as her personal signature. Violet was the colour of the uniforms of her staff and in many letters she painted a violet in place of her signature. One of the varieties of Parma violet available today is named 'Duchesse de Parme', in honour of Marie Louise, and another is called 'Marie-Louise'.

Marie Louise commissioned the monks at the Monastery of the Annunciation, who were known for their pharmaceutical skills, to extract the fragrance from the Parma violets and create a perfume just for her. This they did and it became known as 'Violetta di Parma'. The monks jealously guarded the secret of this perfume but about 25 years after the death of Marie Louise, Lodovico Borsari managed to get details of its manufacture and today it is available to all who desire it. One quirk of some violets is the elusive scent of their flowers and this property has been traced to one of the constituents which is able to temporarily desensitize the receptors in the nose. Given the mythology of the violet it should come as no surprise that this compound is called ionone.

The genus *Viola* is sub-divided into pansies, violas and violettas but the distinction between them is not entirely clear. A pansy generally is a very short-lived perennial with a single main stem and the flower usually has a large central blotch. Violas generally have small flowers, are more truly perennial, and have a tufted habit, i.e. produce many shoots from the crown. Violettas also are perennial but have much smaller flowers. Shakespeare certainly considered pansies to be different from violets. In *Hamlet,* Ophelia says to her brother Laertes 'And there's pansies, that's for thoughts' and shortly afterwards says to King Claudius 'I would give you some violets, but they withered all when my father died'. The name 'pansy' is derived from the French 'pensee' meaning 'thought'. It was so named because the flower resembles a human face and in August nods forward as if deep in thought.

It is not clear exactly which species of *Viola* Shakespeare considered a pansy. The pansies cultivated today are known as *Viola x wittrockiana* and are considered to be hybrids of *V. tricolor* (Heartsease or wild pansy), *V. altaica* and *V. lutea* (mountain pansy). The development of the modern pansy was begun in the early 19th century and one of the leading players was William Thompson, gardener to Lord Gambier. He began crossing different violas and in 1839 found a seedling that was quite different from all the others: it had a large blotch without which most people do not consider a pansy to be a pansy. He called it 'Medora'. Today, there are many different kinds of pansies available and they come in an amazing range of sizes and colour combinations.

The last violet to be considered here is the one known as the shrinking violet, the term used to describe someone who is unassertive. Its etymological origin is unclear but it may be derived from the fact that the violet is a delicate flower that wilts and bruises easily. Whatever the origin of the term, it certainly did not apply to Napoleon!

Peas, Sweet Or Otherwise

Mention the word 'peas' and most people will think of sweet peas (*Lathyrus odoratus*), grown for their exquisitely scented blooms, or the pea (*Pisum sativum*) that we eat as a vegetable. However, there are many other 'peas' and these include the edible chickpea (*Cicer arietinum*), Sturt's desert pea (*Swainsona formosa*) that is the emblem of South Australia, the everlasting pea (*Lathyrus latifolius*), the spring pea (*Lathyrus vernus*), etc. All of them belong to the family of plants that used to be known as the Leguminosae, or legumes, and that now is called the Papilionaceae. This name is derived from the Latin word for a butterfly, *papilio*, in reference to the characteristic shape of the flowers. Another characteristic of all the legumes is the incorporation of the seeds in a pod, the best examples being peas. Whilst the morphological differences between *Pisum* and *Lathyrus* might be of no significance to gardeners there is one differentiating feature of importance. Although the pods of *Lathyrus* species can be eaten, they contain a compound that can cause paralysis.

The edible pea has been used as a food since ancient times. Archaeologists have found them at sites of early civilizations in Syria, Turkey and Egypt and believe that they came to Europe with the spread of Neolithic agriculture. Up until the Middle Ages it was the practice to store the dried peas and eat them as needed. During the 16th century the practice developed of eating the peas 'green', i.e. while they are immature and right after they are picked. This was especially true in France and England where the eating of green peas was said to be 'both a fashion and a madness'. The world's first sweet tasting pea was developed in the 18th century by amateur breeder Thomas Knight who lived at Downton near Salisbury. Modern garden pea varieties can be traced back to Knight's original selection. A more recent development is the breeding of edible-pod peas that are eaten as whole tender pods without shelling. This is possible because they lack the fibrous inner lining that is found in the pods of garden peas. These edible-pod peas are referred to variously as snow peas, sugar peas, China peas, mange-tout and sugar snap peas. The latter have fuller, fatter pods with individual peas that are allowed to develop more than the other four types that have flatter pods.

The first written description of the flower that we know as the sweet pea (*Lathyrus odoratus*) can be traced back to the publication in 1697 of a book written by a Sicilian monk, Father Franciscus Cupani, and called *Hortus Catholicus*. This publication came to the attention of Dr Robert Uvedale, the headmaster of Enfield Grammar School and a keen grower of 'exotic' garden plants. Uvedale wrote to Cupani in 1699 to congratulate him on his text and the monk responded by sending him some seeds of *L. odoratus*. It is worth noting that Cupani also sent seeds to Casper Commelin, a botanist at the medical school in Amsterdam, who published a book a few years later that contains the first illustration of the sweet pea. Leonard Plukenet, the gardener of William and Mary at Hampton Court Palace obtained samples from Uvedale and dried specimens from his herbarium are stored at the Natural History Museum in London.

The poet John Keats (1795–1821) is credited with the first use of the name 'sweet pea' for *Lathyrus odoratus* when he wrote:

Here are sweet peas, on tip-toe for a flight:
With wings of gentle flush o'er delicate white,
And taper fingers catching at all things,
To bind them all about with tiny rings.

By a curious twist of fate, Keats went to school in Enfield where sweet peas had been grown for the first time in England 100 years before. The second line in the above verse is particularly interesting. The pea flower has five petals: a large upper petal or standard, two wings, and the keel that consists of two small petals joined together. Often these petals are not the same colour and the original Sicilian sweet pea was a maroon and violet bicolour. However, the sweet pea is notorious for throwing off colour variants and white forms are known. It could be such a flower that Keats is describing. However the use of the word 'wings' may be an early reference to the floral structure or it could be an accidental metaphor.

Lathyrus odoratus quickly became a popular garden flower and in the 1720s there were numerous references to seedsmen selling 'sweet sented pease'. A catalogue from the 1730s lists purple, white and variegated forms, the latter having white and rose-coloured flowers and commonly called the Painted Lady. These were natural variants for breeding proper did not occur until the late 19th century. The first breeder of importance was Henry Eckford (1823–1905) from Wem in Shropshire. He developed dozens of fragrant varieties with sturdier stems and larger flowers and called them Grandifloras. In 1900, Silas Cole was the head gardener to the Earl Spencer at Althorp House in Northamptonshire. He was growing the Eckford variety 'Prima Donna' when he spotted a variant that had a ruffled standard, large wings and larger more flamboyant blooms. He called this variant 'Countess Spencer'.

The Spencer variant became an overnight success and set in motion a quest that continues to this day for even larger, wavy-edged flowers. However, in the process of developing these, an important characteristic has got lost: the exquisite fragrance that gave rise to the specific epithet '*odorata*'. Modern breeders of sweet peas now are re-introducing scent to the Spencer varieties but this is not always considered a good thing. The great horticulturalist Edward Bowles (1865–1954), also of Enfield (!), complained;

> A dining-table decorated heavily with sweet peas spoils my dinner as I taste sweet peas with every course, and they are horrible as a sauce for fish, whilst they ruin the bouquet of a good wine.

As Maggie Campbell-Culver wrote in her book *The Origin of Plants*, this makes them 'the garlic equivalent of the floral world'. I know exactly what she means.

A Plethora Of Primulas

The genus *Primula* is very large and contains over 400 species including a number of old favourites such as primroses (*P. vulgaris*), cowslips (*P. veris*), oxlips (*P. elatior*), auriculas (*P. auricula*) and polyanthus (hybrids). The name comes from Greek mythology: the primula was Paralisos, son of Flora and Priapus, who died of a broken heart over the loss of his sweetheart Melicentra. His parents immortalized him by turning him into the flowers that we know as primroses. The primrose is the *prima rosa* or first rose of the year and its flowers herald the start of a new growing season. It was also named *primaverola*, from *fior di primavera*, the first flower of spring. The name cowslip is derived from 'cuslyppe' which is Old English for cowpat and is a reference to their prevalence in meadows where cows have grazed. The name auricula comes from the old name for these plants which was *Auricula ursis* or bear's ears and reflects the shape of the leaves.

Primroses and cowslips are native to Britain and the earliest written record of them is in Chaucer's *The Canterbury Tales*. In the bawdy *Miller's Tale* there is a description of Alison, the carpenter's wife:

She was a primrose, and a tender chicken
For any lord to lay upon his bed,
Or yet for any good yeoman to wed.

Shakespeare was very familiar with the primulas for he makes numerous references to them in his plays. In The Winter's Tale, Perdita mentions various flowers she wishes to make into a garland for Florizel with whom she is in love:

... pale primroses,
That die unmarried, ere they can behold
Bright Phoebus in his strength.

In *A Midsummer Night's Dream*, Oberon describes the spot where his wife Titania is sleeping as:

I know a bank where the wild thyme blows,
Where oxlips and the nodding violet grows.

Elsewhere in the same play, Shakespeare makes reference to the commonly held belief at the time that cowslips were associated with fairies.

Other references to primulas by Shakespeare occur in Cymbeline, The Two Noble Kinsmen, Macbeth and Hamlet. The latter is by far the most interesting because it is the first reference to the familiar phrase 'the primrose path'. Ophelia tells Laertes to show her

... the steep and thorny way to heaven,
Whiles, like a puff'd and reckless libertine,
Himself the primrose path of dalliance treads,
And reaks not his own rede.

Shakespeare probably got the idea for the concept of the primrose path from the Biblical book of Matthew, 'wide is the gate and broad is the way that leadeth to destruction'. He certainly liked the phrase because he used it again in Macbeth.

In Regency London, hawking various wares was an occupation open to women and a common cry from such street vendors was:

Will you buy my sweet primroses
Two bunches a-penny
All a-growing, all a-blowing
Who will buy my sweet primroses
Two bunches a-penny.

The phrase 'all a-growing' meant that the flowers could be planted by the buyers in their gardens. The flower-sellers, or more likely their children, would have gathered the primroses from the fields near their homes in Islington, Paddington or Lambeth

Auriculas are natives of the upper pastures of the Alps and the Dolomites and it is thought that they were brought to England at the end of the 16th century by Huguenots fleeing persecution in France. The Huguenots were a protestant reform movement that was founded in Geneva and spread into France so it is highly likely that they were familiar with auriculas. However, cultivated auriculas were much prized at the time and some people doubt that the Huguenots could have afforded them. Regardless of how they got here, they proved immensely popular. John Gerard, a gardener and surgeon of some repute, published his *Catalogue* in 1596, the first compilation of all the plants in one garden. In it, he listed 30 different types of Mountain Cowslips, or auriculas, and in 1659 Sir Thomas Hanmer recorded forty types in his *Garden Book*. John Tradescant the Elder, gardener to Charles I, is recorded in 1633 as growing them in his garden at Lambeth and 'improving' them.

A key date in the development of auriculas was 1757. In that year James Thompson from Newcastle-upon-Tyne reported the discovery of a very unusual natural variant with two distinguishing characteristics. The first of these was a new colour never seen before in a flower: clear green. The second was a central ring (or 'centre') of a different colour. This variant was used as one of the parents in many of the hybrid auriculas that were bred subsequently, often in crosses with *P. hirsuta*. These hybrids were characterised by even more new colours for flowers including slate blue, cinnamon and the popular grey-green. Some breeders even began formulating standards of perfection that were based on the ratios of the different zones of the flower.

As country people in England migrated to the northern industrial towns they found that auriculas thrived in the smoky conditions that were prevalent then. Also, manure was freely available in the towns because there were so many working horses. Consequently, the north of England became (literally) a breeding ground for new auriculas. Indeed, the generation of new varieties became so popular that auricula theatres were developed for showing them to best advantage. The tradition began in France and Belgium in the early 17th century and initially an auricula theatre was an open-fronted box with simple shelves designed to protect the flowers from wind and rain. Later versions involved tiered staging and in 19th century England their construction was raised to an art form. The most elaborate, to be found in stately homes, had grand stages with faux-painted curtains and proscenium arches to add drama to the displays.

By contrast with the other primulas, the polyanthus is of garden origin and today probably is a collection of different hybrids whose parentage is drawn from the cowslip, the oxlip and the common primrose. The name 'polyanthus' first appears in print in the late 17th century and, like auriculas, became a popular plant for breeding in the industrial towns of Lancashire and Cheshire.

The native primrose (*P. vulgaris*) was yellow or white and coloured varieties were unknown until the introduction of *P. vulgaris* subspecies *sibthorpii* from Eastern Europe in 1638. This has rose-red, lilac or violet flowers and when it was cultivated alongside the native species gave rise to new colours through inter-breeding. However, it was the early 20th century before botanists and horticulturalists became aware of the full range of natural colours and forms exhibited by primulas. One of the great plant hunters, George Forrest, discovered the species now known as *P. vialli*, *P. forrestii* and *P. caveana*. Around the same time another famous plant hunter, Frank Kingdom Ward, found yet more new species. These included *P. alpicola*, which he called Joseph's Sikkimensis Primula after the biblical coat of many colours, and the giant cowslip (*P. florindae*).

One primula, *P. sonchifolia*, was sent from Burma in 1930 and is noteworthy because it was the first new plant to arrive in Britain by air. Prior to then all new plants had been despatched by sea and often were dead on arrival.

The most famous advocate of primulas must be Benjamin Disraeli (Lord Beaconsfield) whose favourite flower was the common primrose. 19 April is known as Primrose Day because Disraeli died on that date in 1881. According to a contemporary account of his funeral:

> *The coffin lies on its bier in an alcove leading out of the modest hall of Hughenden Manor* (Disraeli's home near High Wycombe, Buckinghamshire). *But of its material, one might almost say of its dimensions, nothing can be seen. It is literally one mass of floral beauty. Here are wreaths from every member of the Royal Family in England including bouquets of primroses sent by the Queen, with an inscription attached to them, saying that they came from Osborne Hill* (in the grounds of the Queen's house on the Isle of Wight), *and that they are of the sort which Lord Beaconsfield loved.*

As someone whose surname is Primrose and who lives close to Hughenden Manor, what could be a more fitting end?

Lily And Solomon: Who Were They?

Lily, of course, is lily of the valley (*Convallaria majalis*) and Solomon is Solomon's seal (*Polygonatum multiflorum* in Europe and *P. biflorum* in North America). Both of them belong to the Family Convallariaceae and some of their close relatives are false Solomon's seal (*Smilacina racemosa*, now *Maianthemum racemosa*), the house plant *Aspidistra*, and *Ophiopogon* which is grown for its near-black foliage. The name of the family is derived from the Latin word *convallis*, meaning valley, which is a little surprising since the natural habitats of the family members are meadows and light woodland.

Lily of the valley has flowers that are not too dissimilar to those of true lilies (*Lilium* species) and so the 'lily' epithet is easy to understand. Some of the other common names for this plant are May lily, Our Lady's tears, lily constancy, ladder-to-heaven and Jacob's ladder. The origin of these names, apart from the first two, is not known. According to one legend, the tears that Mary shed at the cross turned to lilies of the valley hence the name Our Lady's tears. Another legend comes from Sussex where the hermit St Leonard is supposed to have battled the dragon Malitia who was really the devil in disguise. St Leonard was successful in slaying the dragon but not before his adversary's claws had ripped through his armour. Lilies of the valley sprang up from the drops of his blood and to this day people can trace the path of the battle by the blooming of the flowers. Given that blood is red, one might have expected to find the pink-flowered variety at the supposed battle scene! According to folklore, the plant blooms upon the grave of someone who was executed for a crime they did not commit.

The lily of the valley is connected with the Greek goddess Maia. She was the eldest of the Pleiades, the seven daughters of Atlas and Pleione, and the most beautiful and the shyest. In Roman mythology she was the goddess of Spring and the month of May was named for her. The lily of the valley flowers in May, as do may of its relatives, and this is reflected in its Latin name *Convallaria majalis*. The specific epithet 'majalis' or 'maialis' means 'May flowering'. Because of its time of flowering, the lily of the valley is associated with Whitsunday, or Pentecost, the seventh Sunday after Easter which celebrates the Holy Spirit descending to the Apostles. In France, it is the custom to buy for oneself or one's friends a pot or bouquet of lily of the valley during the month of May. Every florist has pots of it and by tradition the pots always are deep and vase-shaped. Bouquets and buttonholes of it are sold on the streets and on May Day (1 May) it is not necessary to buy a licence to be a street vendor.

Lily of the valley has a long history of use for medicinal purposes. Apuleius, a second century herbalist recorded that Apollo made a gift of the plant to Aesculapius, the god of healing. The plant is known to contain two pharmacologically-active substances: convallamarin and convallarin. The latter has a purgative action whereas the former slows the heart and strengthens it in a similar fashion to digoxin from the foxglove. Herbalists prefer to use lily of the valley over the foxglove because it is less toxic, primarily because it is quickly eliminated by the body. John Gerard, the herbalist to King James I, described the preparation of lily of the valley for topical uses:

> *a glasse being filled with the flowers of May Lilies and set in an Ant Hill with the mouth close stopped for a month's space and then taken out, ye shall find a liquor in the glasse which being outwardly applied helps the gout very much.*

This spirit also was considered excellent as an embrocation for sprains and rheumatism.

In 1896, Robert Louis Stevenson incorporated Gerard's prescription into his novel *Kidnapped*. In the opening chapter, the minister of Essendean gives the hero (David Balfour) a piece of paper left for him by his father. Written in red ink is the recipe that mirrors almost exactly those quoted above. Apparently, Stevenson's wife had read about lily of the valley water in a book called *The Compleat Housewife*: or *Accomplish'd Gentlewoman's Companion*. She found it so charming that she interrupted her husband's writing to tell him about it. 'Just what I wanted!' he explained and immediately incorporated it into his novel.

The scent of lily of the valley once was believed seductive enough to lure the nightingale into mating. Even if the nightingales were not impressed by it the French perfumers certainly were. The original perfume incorporating it was made by Coty in the 1930s and was called Muguet des Bois, the common name in French for lily of the valley. The British, with their flair for languages (!), call it 'muggets. Diorissimo, according to its creator Edmond Roudnitska, 'is a pure lily of the valley scent that also has an odour of the woods in which it is found and the indefinable atmosphere of the springtime'. Sounds like marketing hype to me! Other perfumes based on lily of the valley are Guerlain Muguet and Caron Muguet du Bonheur.

Although lily of the valley is native to Britain, Shakespeare makes no mention of it even though it was known to his herbalist contemporaries. However, later poets did write about it and usually it was associated with humility and purity. This certainly was the theme of a hymn called *The Lily of the Valley* that was written in 1881 by a member of the Salvation Army and whose refrain is:

He's the Lily of the Valley, the Bright and Morning Star,
He's the fairest of ten thousand to my soul.

Other ecumenical poets who wrote about the flower include Bishop Richard Mant and the rector of St Stephen's Walbrook, George Croly. Lord Byron described the latter as the Rev. Rowley Powley in *Don Juan*. *The Lily of the*

Valley also was the title of a novel by Honore de Balzac but it certainly was not about humility or purity. This is a tale of life and love in early 19th century France and resurrects one of the common themes of the Romantic Movement in literature: the tension between spiritual and physical love. The lily of the valley to whom the title refers is the Comtesse de Mortsauf. She acts as mentor to the hero of the novel, the young Felix de Vandenesse, who probably is a representation of the adolescent Balzac.

Solomon's seal gets its name from its rootstock which has scars on it from the previous years' growth. These scars resemble the old fashioned seals that were used to imprint the wax that sealed letters. Some think that the rootstock when cut resembles Hebrew characters or even the Star of David. Others think that the scars resemble the signet ring that gave King Solomon his power to rule. The rationale for the Latin name for the plant, *Polygonatum*, is better understood. It means 'many-angled' and refers to the shape of the rootstock.

The roots of Solomon's seal are very starchy and have been used as a substitute for potato whilst the shoots can be boiled and eaten like asparagus. Medicinally, the powdered root has been used as a poultice for bruises and as a popular cure for black eyes. According to John Gerard the herbalist:

> *The roots of Solomon's Seal, stamped while it is fresh and greene and applied, taketh away in one night or two at most, any bruise, blacke or blew spots gotten by fals or women's wilfulness in stumbling upin their hastie husband's fists, or such like.*

Clearly, domestic violence was a problem in the 16th century as much as it is now. Gerard goes on to say that for internal bruises and broken bones the root should be taken in wine but for external bruises it should be applied 'outwardly in the manner of a pultis'. In the latter case it would have been mixed with some animal fat before application.

According to the Elizabethan herbalist Nicholas Culpepper;

> *...the diluted water of the whole plant used to the face or other parts of the skin cleanses it from freckles, spots or any marks whatever, leaving*

the place fresh, fair and lovely, for which purpose it is much used by the Italian ladies and is the principal ingredient of most of the cosmetics and beauty washes advertised by perfumers at high price.

There is no scientific basis for these claims and so it is interesting that in North America the Cherokee Indians used it for much the same purpose.

At the outset we posed a question: Lily and Solomon, who were they? The answer should be clear by now. Lily was not a person but just a flower that resembles a lily and Solomon may have been King Solomon but, there again, he might not have been.

The Close Of The Year

Remembering The Fallen: The Poppy, The Rose And The Lone Pine

Since 1919 the poppy has been the symbol of Remembrance in Britain and the Commonwealth countries. It is a visual pledge to never forget the citizens of these countries who died in war and other military operations that we might be free. Every year around 11 November, the date when the First World War ended, red cloth poppies will appear in lapels. But, how many of the wearers know how the poppy became associated with the act of Remembrance?

The story begins in 1915 in Ypres in the western part of Belgium (Flanders). This region saw some of the bloodiest fighting of the First World War and the numbers of wounded and injured on both sides were unbelievably high. Colonel John McCrae was a surgeon attached to the 1st Canadian Field Artillery Brigade and had seen and heard enough suffering in his dressing station to last him a lifetime. One day during a lull he vented his anguish by composing one of the most memorable war poems ever written.

In Flanders' Fields the poppies blow
Between the crosses, row on row,
That mark our place; and in the sky
The larks, still bravely singing, fly
Scarce heard amid the guns below.

We are the dead. Short days ago
We lived, felt dawn, saw sunset glow,
Loved, and were loved, and now we lie
In Flanders' Fields.

Take up our quarrel with the foe:
To you from failing hands we throw
The torch; be yours to hold it high.
If ye break faith with us who die
We shall not sleep, though poppies grow
In Flanders' Fields

The red poppies that McCrae saw in Flanders are annuals whose seed only germinates in soil that has been disturbed. After the battles were over and the dead had been buried there was plenty of freshly-turned soil. In that Spring of 1915 vast swathes of poppies appeared: new life where shortly before there had been almost certain death. An American lady, Moira Michael, was so impressed with McCrae's poem that she wrote a reply entitled 'We shall keep the Faith'.

Oh! You who sleep in Flanders' Fields,
Sleep sweet – to rise anew;
We caught the torch you threw;
And holding high we kept
The faith with those who died.
We cherish, too, the poppy red
That grows on fields where valour led.
It seems to signal to the skies
That blood of heroes never dies,
But lends a luster to the red
Of the flowers that blooms above the dead
In Flanders' Fields.
And now the torch and poppy red
Wear in honour of our dead
Fear not that ye have died for naught
We've learned the lesson that ye taught
In Flanders' Fields.

Moira Michael worked for the YMCA and in November 1918 hosted a meeting of YMCA wartime secretaries from other countries. Several of the secretaries gave her a gift of $10 in appreciation of her efforts to brighten up the headquarters with flowers. Touched by the gesture she went out and purchased 25 red silk poppies. When she returned to duty at the YMCA headquarters several of the conference delegates asked if they could have one of the poppies to wear. Keeping one of the poppies for her coat collar she gave out the rest of them. Thus a tradition that many think of as British actually had an American origin. The French secretary at the conference conceived the idea of selling artificial poppies to raise money to help needy soldiers and their families. The practice was adopted and continues to this day. The British Legion was formed in 1919 to foster the interests of ex-servicemen and the first president of the organization, Field Marshal Earl Haig, adopted the red poppy as the emblem of Remembrance.

Not long after McCrae wrote his poem, the Reverend David Railton was serving as a British army chaplain on the Western front. One day he came upon a grave marked by a rough cross that carried the legend 'An Unknown British Soldier' written in pencil. He was so moved by this that after the war he wrote to the Dean of Westminster. In his letter he proposed that an unidentified British soldier from the battlefields in France be buried with due ceremony in Westminster Abbey 'amongst the kings' to represent the many thousands of Empire dead. In November 1920, at a chapel near Arras in France, the bodies of four unknown British soldiers were presented to two army officers. They selected one of the bodies to be placed in a coffin bearing the legend 'A British Warrior who fell in the Great War'. The coffin was transferred with full military honours to Westminster Abbey where it was interred with soil from each of the main battlefields. When Elizabeth Bowes-Lyon married the future King George VI in 1923, she laid her bouquet at the Tomb of the Unknown Soldier on her way into the Abbey. This gesture has been copied by every royal bride married in the Abbey since then except that now they lay their bouquet on the way back from the altar.

Other nations that fought in the Great War also have chosen to establish memorials to unknown soldiers. In 1921 the United States began their process at a ceremony in the Hotel de Ville at Chalons-sur-Marne. Once again there were four bodies from different French battlefields. Sergeant Edward Younger, who had been charged with selecting one of the bodies for the ultimate honour, entered the room bearing a spray of white roses symbolizing death. After circling all of the coffins he indicated his choice by placing the roses upon it. These roses accompanied the coffin until it was interred in Arlington National Cemetery near Washington DC. In this cemetery there are memorials to US soldiers who fell in other military campaigns and each contains the body of an unknown soldier. Following the tradition established in France, a soldier is asked to choose one body from a selection of four and to indicate his choice by placing a spray of white roses upon it. These roses then are buried with the body.

Among Britain's allies in the Great War were soldiers from the Australia and New Zealand Army Core (ANZAC). Their first major battle was against the Turks at Gallipoli in 1915. One major offensive was at Plateau 400, dubbed Lone Pine ridge by the 1st Australian Infantry Division because it was dominated by a single Allepo pine tree (*Pinus halepensis*). The Turks had cut down all the other trees to cover their trenches. In three days of bloody fighting the Australians lost more than 2,000 men and the Turkish losses were estimated at 7,000. Some of the surviving soldiers took pinecones as souvenirs and at least two of these cones found their way back to Australia.

One of the cones ended up in the hands of Mrs Emma Gray who lived near Warrnambool in Victoria. In the late 20s she planted seeds from the cone and four seedlings developed. One seedling was planted at the Shrine of Remembrance in Melbourne and another at the Soldiers Memorial Hall at The Sisters. The other two were planted in public gardens. The second cone was sent by one of the soldiers to his mother, Mrs McMullen, in Inverell in New South Wales. She kept the cone for 13 years before planting the seeds. Only two seedlings developed and one of them was presented to the town of Inverell. The other seedling was presented to the Department of the Interior in Canberra. In 1934 it was planted by the Duke of Gloucester in the grounds of the magnificent Australian War Memorial. Today it stands over 20 metres (60 feet) in height and is flanked by a bronze sculpture of Bellona, a Roman goddess of war, that was donated by the artist Sir Bertram Mackennal in recognition of the gallantry of the Australian soldiers at Gallipoli.

Since the 1980s Allepo pines have been grown by both seed and grafting techniques from material collected from the tree outside the Australian War Memorial. In 1990, two of these trees were taken back to Gallipoli by war veterans who attended the memorial service to commemorate the 75th anniversary of the battle of Lone Pine. Many of the other trees that have been raised are available for sale in garden centres in Australia where they carry the logo … LEST WE FORGET.

Tall Tales At Christmas

The end of the calendar year is the time that we associate with the singing of carols and one of the many popular carols is named after two plants that we associate with Christmas: the *Holly and the Ivy*. The practice of using holly dates back to at least 1000 BCE. The disciples of Zoroastrianism, the religion of Persia before Islam, believed that the sun never cast a shadow on the holly and thus was a symbol of good health. Later, the Romans used it during the feast of Saturnalia in mid-December when they celebrated the winter solstice. Because the holly represented good health, Pagan Romans sent sprigs of it to friends to wish them good health.

When the Romans became Christians they continued to use holly to decorate buildings in December but now it was to celebrate Christmas. Supposedly this was not done for convenience but because the Crown of Thorns made for Jesus was woven of prickly holly leaves. In this instance holly did not symbolise good health! As folklore has it, the berries of the holly were yellow but since the crucifixion they have been stained red with the blood of Jesus. It is a nice story but today you can find holly with berries that are red or yellow as well as white and black.

Britain is unique in having a number of true holly woods and these can be found in Epping Forest, the Welsh Marches and parts of Cumbria. Also, at Kew Gardens there is a Holly Walk laid out in 1874. It has the largest collection of hollies in Europe and contains over 56 species and hybrids. At Tenbury Wells in Herefordshire there even is an annual holly market.

Ivy has been popular for decoration over the centuries and once was thought to offer protection against house goblins that were at their most malicious in winter. Like holly, ivy has been used since pre-Christian times because evergreens were associated with the power of eternity. In pagan times it was thought that holly was a male plant and ivy a female plant. An old tradition from the Midlands of England says that if holly is brought into the house first then the man will be dominant over the coming year. Should the ivy be brought in first then his wife will reign supreme (what's new?).

Another plant associated with Christmas is mistletoe. The custom of kissing under the mistletoe derives from a Norse myth that decreed that no harm would befall anyone standing beneath this plant and that they should receive only tokens of affection. Bringing the mistletoe into the house was a good idea for it is much pleasanter to stand with one's loved one under a sprig hanging up in a warm house than under a bunch of it growing in an apple tree in a cold wet garden or orchard.

The traditional Christmas plant in the United States is not holly. It is the poinsettia whose glory comes from the brightly coloured, petal-like leaves (bracts) that surround each tiny cluster of green flowers. In the wild the bracts are scarlet but breeders have developed varieties in shades of red, pink and cream. Anyone who has visited North America at Christmas will have been impressed with the very striking displays in which potted poinsettias are used *en masse*. They would be even more impressed if they saw poinsettias cultivated in the ground where they can be maintained as 10 foot shrubs by hard pruning.

The poinsettia (*Euphorbia pulcherrima*) is a native of Mexico. The Aztecs, who used the plant's milky sap in the treatment of fevers, called it *cuetlaxochitl*. This translates as 'the flower of the short days' and is very appropriate as poinsettias only flower when there are less than 12 hours of daylight. This means that in countries in the southern hemisphere where poinsettias are popular at Christmas, e.g. Australia, the plants have to be forced into flower. Latin Americans call the poinsettia *la flor de Noche Buena*, the flower of the Holy Night. Supposedly, a young Mexican girl had nothing to offer the

Christ Child at the Christmas Eve mass but a posy of leaves and grasses that she had collected. Some in the congregation sniggered as she laid her posy at the altar forgetting that God accepts any gift given with love. She was rewarded with a miracle: her humble weeds changed into scarlet flowers of such beauty that they outshone the other flowers. This story gave rise to the specific epithet for *pulcherrima* means 'most beautiful'.

Joel Poinsett (1779–1851), one of the founders of the Smithsonian Institute in Washington DC, was the first US ambassador to Mexico. He was so taken with the plant we now call the poinsettia that he had some shipped back to his plantation in South Carolina. The climate there suited the poinsettia and soon there were enough plants for them to be distributed to friends. Eventually one found its way to Robert Buist, a plantsman from Pennsylvania who was the first to sell it under its botanical name of *Euphorbia pulcherrima*. In terms of names, the poinsettia is a rare example of a common name honouring the 'discoverer' of a plant: it is more usual for them to be remembered via the Latin name.

Evergreen fir trees, or their more recent artificial representations, have been used for thousands of years to celebrate winter festivals. Nobody is really sure when they were first used as Christmas trees but there is documented evidence that they were used for this purpose in Latvia at the start of the 16th century. Christmas trees as we know them may have started as the Paradise Trees that represented the Garden of Eden in the German Mystery Plays that took place during the Middle Ages. These plays told Bible stories to people who could not read. Christmas trees became popular in Britain in 1841 when Queen Victoria's consort Prince Albert, who was German, set one up in Windsor Castle.

A Christmas tree that is unique in the strict sense of the word is the Glastonbury thorn. This particular specimen of hawthorn (*Crataegnus monogyna*) is unusual in flowering twice in the year: once as normal on old wood in Spring and once in the Winter on new wood. In the Middle Ages, the local populace of Glastonbury considered this tree to be miraculous and word of it reached King Henry VIII. In 1535 he sent an advisor to confirm the existence of the tree that 'blossoms at Christmas, mindful of our Lord'. After this, the tree became famous. Not surprisingly, during the English

Civil war, troops loyal to Oliver Cromwell cut down the tree and burned it. However, cuttings had been taken and one of these was planted in secret in the grounds of Glastonbury Abbey.

One Christmas, the Bishop of Bath and Wells sent a budded branch of the Glastonbury thorn to Queen Anne, the consort of King James I. The Vicar and Mayor of Glastonbury continue this tradition to this day. These branches were taken from the hawthorn planted in the Abbey grounds until this tree died in 1991. Fortunately, in the early 20th century, the head gardener of the Abbey had propagated cuttings and one of these is used to provide Queen Elizabeth II with the blooms that grace her breakfast table.

There are many myths surrounding the Glastonbury thorn. One concerns Joseph of Arimathea who supposedly visited Glastonbury after the crucifixion of Jesus. He had a staff that had been cut from the tree that provided the Crown of Thorns. Resting on a hill, Joseph thrust his staff into the ground where it promptly grew roots and became the holy thorn of Glastonbury. An interesting story but the truth likely is more mundane. A pilgrim probably brought it back from the Middle East unaware that the dual-flowering properties of his introduction would cause such a stir.